Working Papers
for use with

Sixteenth Canadian Edition

Fundamental
ACCOUNTING
PRINCIPLES

Volume 1

SIXTEENTH CANADIAN EDITION

Kermit D. Larson
University of Texas—Austin

Heidi Dieckmann
Kwantlen Polytechnic University—British Columbia

Revised by
Laura Dallas
Kwantlen Polytechnic University—British Columbia

Reviewed by
Rhonda Heninger
Southern Alberta Institute of Technology—Alberta

Mc
Graw
Hill
Education

correct

1, 2, 3

**Working Papers for use with
Fundamental Accounting Principles
Volume 1
Sixteenth Canadian Edition**

ISBN-13: 978-1-26-030596-8
ISBN-10: 1-26-030596-1

1 2 3 4 5 WEB 21 20 19

Printed and bound in Canada.

Care has been taken to trace ownership of copyright material contained in this text; however, the
publisher will welcome any information that enables them to rectify any reference or credit for
subsequent editions.

Product Director: Rhondda McNabb
Senior Portfolio Manager: Alwynn Pinard
Senior Marketing Manager: Loula March
Content Developer: Shalini Khanna
Senior Portfolio Associate: Stephanie Giles
Supervising Editor: Jessica Barnoski
Plant Production Coordinator: Michelle Saddler
Manufacturing Production Coordinator: Jason Stubner
Cover Design: Michelle Losier
Cover Image: Rachel Idzerda
Page Layout: Aptara®, Inc.
Printer: Webcom, Ltd.

Contents

Quick Study 1-1

_____
_____
_____
_____
_____
_____
_____
_____
_____
_____
_____
_____
_____
_____

Quick Study 1-2

a. _____

b. _____

c. _____

d. _____

e. _____
_____

Quick Study 1-3

a. _____
b. _____
c. _____
d. _____
e. _____
f. _____

Quick Study 1-4

1. _____	5. _____
2. _____	6. _____
3. _____	7. _____
4. _____	

Name: _____

Quick Study 1-5

1. _____
2. _____
3. _____
4. _____
5. _____
6. _____
7. _____
8. _____

Quick Study 1-6

_____
_____
_____
_____
_____
_____
_____
_____
_____
_____
_____
_____
_____
_____
_____
_____
_____
_____

Quick Study 1-7

1. _____
2. _____
3. _____

Quick Study 1-8

1. _____   4. _____
2. _____   5. _____
3. _____

Fundamental Accounting Principles, 16ce, Working Papers

Quick Study 1-9

	1.	Delco performed work for a client located in China and collected 8,450,000 RMB (renminbi, the Chinese currency), the equivalent of about $1,320,000 Canadian. Delco recorded it as 8,450,000.
	2.	Delco collected $180,000 from a customer on December 20, 2020, for work to be done in February 2021. The $180,000 was recorded as revenue during 2020. Delco's year-end is December 31.
	3.	Delco's December 31, 2020, balance sheet showed total assets of $840,000 and liabilities of $1,120,000. The income statements for the past six years have shown a trend of increasing losses.
	4.	Included in Delco's assets was land and a building purchased for $310,000 and reported on the balance sheet at $470,000.
	5.	Delco's owner, Tom Del, consistently buys personal supplies and charges them to the company.

Quick Study 1-10

Assets	=	Liabilities	+	Equity
a.				
b.				
c.				

Quick Study 1-11

Assets	=	Liabilities	+	Equity
a.				
b.				
c.				

Quick Study 1-12

All-In Servicing
Income Statement
For Month Ended April 30, 2020

Revenues	$300
Expenses	?
Profit (loss)	?

All-In Servicing
Statement of Changes in Equity
For Month Ended April 30, 2020

Tim Allin, capital, April 1		$ 50
Investments by owner	$ 30	
Profit	?	?
Total		$255
Less: Withdrawals by owner		?
Tim Allin, capital, April 30		?

All-In Servicing
Balance Sheet
April 30, 2020

Assets		Liabilities	
Cash	$ 60	Accounts payable	$ 25
Equipment	?	**Equity**	
		Tim Allin, capital	?
		Total liabilities	
Total assets	$265	and equity	?

Fundamental Accounting Principles, 16ce, Working Papers

Quick Study 1-12 (Concluded)

Part b.

All-In Servicing
Income Statement
For Month Ended May 31, 2020

Revenues .... 135 ?

Expenses .... $ 85

Profit (loss) .... 50 ?

(handwritten: ? − 85 = 50)

All-In Servicing
Statement of Changes in Equity
For Month Ended May 31, 2020

Tim Allin, capital, May 1 .... 240 ?

  Investments by owner .... $ 60

  Profit .... 50 ? | $110

Total .... 350 ?

Less: Withdrawals by owner 75

Tim Allin, capital, May 31 .... 275 ?

All-In Servicing
Balance Sheet
May 31, 2020

Assets		**Liabilities**	
Cash	$120	Accounts payable	$ 45
Equipment	200 ?	**Equity**	
		Tim Allin, capital	275 ?
		Total liabilities	
Total assets	320 ?	and equity	320 ?

Quick Study 1-13

1. $5000 _____

2. $12000 _____

_____

(handwritten: 240)

Chapter 1

Quick Study 1-14

	Assets	=	Liabilities	+	Equity
a.	increase / Decrease				
b.	Increase		Increase		
c.	Decrease		Decrease		
d.			Increase		Decrease
e.	Decrease				Decrease

Quick Study 1-15

BS	1. Supplies		IS	8. Utilities expense
IS	2. Supplies expense		BS	9. Furniture
BS	3. Accounts receivable		IS	10. Revenue
BS	4. Accounts payable		IS	11. Rent revenue
BS	5. Equipment		IS	12. Salaries expense
SCE	6. Tim Roadster's withdrawals			13. Tim Roadster's investments
BS	7. Notes payable			14. Profit

Quick Study 1-16

_____ 1. Total revenues
_____ 2. Total operating expenses
_____ 3. Profit
_____ 4. Total assets
_____ 5. Total liabilities
_____ 6. Tim Roadster, capital (April 30, 2020)
_____ 7. Total liabilities and equity

Fundamental Accounting Principles, 16ce, Working Papers

Quick Study 1-17

Not on BS	1.	Loss	$ 2
Not on BS	2.	Rent expense	22
liability	3.	Rent payable	6
asset	4.	Accounts receivable	14
Not on BS	5.	Paul Sangha's investments in May	30
Not on BS	6.	Interest income	2
Not on BS	7.	Paul Sangha's, capital, May 1, 2020	0
asset	8.	Repair supplies	5
liability	9.	Notes payable	25
Not on BS	10.	Paul Sangha's withdrawals in May	5
asset	11.	Truck	15
Not on BS	12.	Consulting revenue	18
equity	13.	Paul Sangha, capital, May 31, 2020	$23
asset	14.	Cash	20

income statement (note by #12)

revenue   -   expense   =   loss / gain
) $22
    18

= $20   = $22   = $ −2

Capital

+30
−5
−2 (from loss)

= $23

Quick Study 1-18

Income Statement

Statement of Changes in Equity

Balance Sheet

Name: _____

Exercise 1-1

a. _____
b. _____
c. _____
d. _____
e. _____
f. _____
g. _____

Exercise 1-2

External Users	Decisions
1.	
2.	
3.	
4.	

Internal Users	Decisions
1.	
2.	
3.	
4.	

Name: _____

Exercise 1-3

Accounting Role	Typical Day
(1) External auditor	
(2) Controller	
(3) Tax Specialist	

Fundamental Accounting Principles, 16ce, Working Papers

Chapter 1

Name: _____

Exercise 1-4

a. _____
_____
_____
_____
_____
_____
_____
_____
_____
_____
_____
_____
_____
_____

b. _____
_____
_____
_____
_____
_____
_____
_____
_____
_____
_____
_____
_____
_____
_____
_____

c. _____
_____
_____
_____
_____
_____
_____
_____
_____
_____
_____
_____
_____
_____

Chapter 1

Name: _____

Exercise 1-5

1. _____

2. _____

3. _____

4. _____

Fundamental Accounting Principles, 16ce, Working Papers

Exercise 1-6

Balance Sheet			Income Statement		Statement of Changes in Equity
Assets	Liabilities	Owner's Equity	Revenue	Expenses	

Chapter 1

Exercise 1-7

a. _____

b. _____

c. _____

_____

_____

d. _____

_____

_____

Exercise 1-8

	(a)	(b)	(c)	(d)	(e)
Equity, January 1	$ -0-	$ -0-	$ -0-	$ -0-	
Owner's investments during the year	60,000		31,500	37,500	140,000
Profit (loss) for the year	15,750	30,500	(4,500)		(8,000)
Owner's withdrawals during the year		(27,000)	(20,000)	(15,750)	(63,000)
Equity, December 31	56,000	49,500		32,000	171,000

Name: _____

Exercise 1-9

Income Statement		

Exercise 1-10

Statement of Changes in Equity		

Analysis component:

_____

_____

_____

_____

_____

Name: _____

	Balance Sheet		

Analysis component:

_____
_____
_____
_____
_____

Chapter 1   Name: _____

Exercise 1-12

Income Statement		

Exercise 1-13

Statement of Changes in Equity		

Analysis component:

_____
_____
_____
_____

Name: _____

Balance Sheet

Analysis component:

_____

_____

_____

_____

_____

Chapter 1 Name: _____

Exercise 1-15

(a) Profit (Loss) = [ ]
  Supporting Calculations: _____

_____

_____

_____

_____

_____

_____

(b) Profit (Loss) = [ ]
  Supporting Calculations: _____

_____

_____

_____

_____

_____

_____

(c) Profit (Loss) = [ ]
  Supporting Calculations: _____

_____

_____

_____

_____

_____

_____

(d) Profit (Loss) = [ ]
  Supporting Calculations: _____

_____

_____

_____

_____

_____

Chapter 1

Exercise 1-16

(a) Assets =
   Equity =

   Supporting Calculations: _____

_____

_____

_____

_____

_____

_____

(b) Liabilities =
   Equity =

   Supporting Calculations: _____

_____

_____

_____

_____

_____

_____

Exercise 1-17

	ASSETS			=	LIABILITIES	+	EQUITY
CASH	+	ACCOUNTS RECEIVABLE	+	OFFICE SUPPLIES =	ACCOUNTS PAYABLE	+	KATIE COPP, CAPITAL
(a)							
(b)							
(c)							
(d)							
(e)							
(f)							

Name: _____

Exercise 1-18

		ASSETS			=	LIABILITIES	+	EQUITY
CASH	+	ACCOUNTS RECEIVABLE	+	PARTS SUPPLIES	+ EQUIPMENT =	ACCOUNTS PAYABLE	+	STACEY COMEAU, CAPITAL
(a)								
(b)								
(c)								
(d)								
(e)								
(f)								
(g)								
(h)								
(i)								

Exercise 1-19

a. _____

b. _____

c. _____

d. _____

e. _____

f. _____

g. _____

		ASSETS			=	LIABILITIES	+	EQUITY	
CASH	+	ACCOUNTS RECEIVABLE	+ SUPPLIES +	EQUIP-MENT	=	ACCOUNTS PAYABLE	+	MAILIN MOON, CAPITAL	EXPLANATIO OF EQUITY TRANSACTIO
(a)									
(b)									
(c)									
(d)									
(e)									
(f)									
(g)									

Name: _____

Exercise 1-21

Mailin Moon – Freelance Writing
Income Statement
For Month Ended March 31, 2020

Revenues:
    Freelance writing revenue ....
Operating expenses:
    Salaries expense ....
    Rent expense .... _____
       Total operating expenses ....
Profit ....

Mailin Moon – Freelance Writing
Statement of Changes in Equity
For Month Ended March 31, 2020

Mailin Moon, capital, March 1 ....
Add: Investment by owner ....
Profit ....
Mailin Moon, capital, March 31 ....

Mailin Moon – Freelance Writing
Balance Sheet
March 31, 2020

Assets		Liabilities	
Cash..............................		Accounts payable...................................	
Accounts receivable			
Supplies........................			
Equipment....................			
		Equity	
		Mailin Moon, capital...............................	
Total assets.................. _____		Total liabilities and equity......................	

Analysis component:

_____
_____
_____
_____
_____
_____
_____

Name: _____

Exercise 1-22

ASSETS					=	LIABILITIES	+	EQUITY	
CASH	+	ACCOUNTS RECEIVABLE	+	SUPPLIES	+	EQUIP-MENT	=	ACCOUNTS PAYABLE	+	ALI OMAR, CAPITAL	EXPLANATION OF EQUITY TRANSACTION
(a)									
(b)									
(c)									
(d)									
(e)									
(f)									
(g)									
(h)									
(i)									

Fundamental Accounting Principles, 16ce, Working Papers

Income Statement

Statement of Changes in Equity

Balance Sheet

Name: _____

Exercise 1-23 (Concluded)

Analysis component:

_____
_____
_____
_____
_____
_____
_____
_____
_____
_____

Name: _____

Exercise 1-24

	ASSETS				=	LIABILITIES	+	EQUITY	
CASH	+	ACCOUNTS RECEIVABLE	+	SUPPLIES	+	EQUIP-MENT	=	ACCOUNTS PAYABLE	+	NATALIE GOLD, CAPITAL	EXPLANATION OF EQUITY TRANSACTION
Bal. $6,000	$1,200	$1,900	$6,500	$4,000	$11,600	
(a)						
(b)						
(c)						
(d)						
(e)						
(f)						
(g)						
(h)						

Name: _____

Income Statement

Statement of Changes in Equity

Fundamental Accounting Principles, 16ce, Working Papers

Exercise 1-25 (Concluded)

Balance Sheet

Analysis component:

_____

_____

_____

_____

_____

Name: _____

Problem 1-1A

Characteristic	Type of Business Organization		
	Sole Proprietorship	Partnership	Corporation
Limited liability			
Unlimited liability			
Owners are shareholders			
Owners are partners			
Taxed as a separate legal entity			

Problem 1-2A

EMAIL

To: _____

From: _____

Subject: _____

_____
_____
_____
_____
_____
_____
_____
_____
_____
_____
_____
_____
_____
_____
_____
_____
_____
_____
_____
_____
_____
_____
_____
_____
_____
_____
_____

Chapter 1

Problem 1-3A

2019 Profit (Loss) = [   ]
   Supporting Calculations: _____

_____
_____
_____
_____
_____
_____
_____
_____
_____

Problem 1-4A

_____

Income Statement

Name: _____

Problem 1-4A (Concluded)

Statement of Changes in Equity

Balance Sheet

Analysis component:

_____
_____
_____
_____
_____
_____

Name: _____

Income Statement

Statement of Changes in Equity

Name: _____

Problem 1 5A (Concluded)

Balance Sheet

Analysis component:

_____

_____

_____

_____

_____

Problem 1-6A

Part 1

Balance Sheet

Name: _____

Problem 1-6A (Concluded)

Balance Sheet

Part 2

Profit (Loss) Calculation: _____

_____

_____

_____

_____

_____

_____

_____

_____

_____

_____

Analysis component:

_____

_____

_____

_____

_____

_____

Chapter 1   Name: _____

Problem 1-7A

Part 1: Company A
(a) _____
_____
_____
_____

(b) _____
_____
_____
_____
_____
_____
_____
_____

(c) _____
_____
_____
_____
_____
_____

Part 2: Company B
(a) _____
_____
_____
_____

(b) _____
_____
_____
_____
_____

(c) _____
_____
_____
_____
_____

Name: _____

Problem 1-7A (Continued)

Part 3: Company C

_____
_____
_____
_____
_____
_____
_____
_____
_____
_____
_____
_____
_____
_____
_____
_____
_____

Part 4: Company D

_____
_____
_____
_____
_____
_____
_____
_____
_____
_____
_____
_____
_____
_____
_____
_____

Name: _____

Problem 1-7A (Concluded)

Part 5: Company E

_____
_____
_____
_____
_____
_____
_____
_____

_____
_____
_____
_____
_____
_____
_____
_____
_____

Fundamental Accounting Principles, 16ce, Working Papers

Name: _____

Problem 1-8A

Parts 1 and 2

CASH	+	ACCOUNTS RECEIVABLE	+	OFFICE SUPPLIES	+	OFFICE EQUIPMENT	+	BUILDING	=	ACCOUNTS PAYABLE	+	NOTES PAYABLE	+	GEORGE LITTLECHILD, CAPITAL		EXPLANATION OF EQUITY TRANSACTION
		ASSETS								**LIABILITIES**				**EQUITY**		
(a)																
(b)																
Bal.																
(c)																
Bal.																
(d)																
Bal.																
(e)																
Bal.																
(f)																
Bal.																
(g)																
Bal.																
(h)																
Bal.																
(i)																
Bal.																
(j)																
Bal.																
(k)																
Bal.																
(l)																
Bal.																

Name: _____

Problem 1-8A (Concluded)

Part 3

Littlechild Enterprises
Income Statement
For Month Ended March 31, 2020

Revenues :
   Service revenue...
Operating expenses:
   Wages expense ....
   Advertising expense ....
     Total operating expenses ....
Loss ....

Littlechild Enterprises
Statement of Changes in Equity
For Month Ended March 31, 2020

George Littlechild, capital, March 1
Add: Investment by owner
   Total
Less: Withdrawal by owner
Loss
George Littlechild, capital, March 31

Littlechild Enterprises
Balance Sheet
March 31, 2020

Assets		Liabilities	
Cash		Accounts payable	
Accounts receivable		Notes payable	
Office supplies		Total liabilities	
Office equipment			
Building		Equity	
		George Littlechild, capital	
Total assets		Total liabilities and equity	

Analysis component:

_____
_____
_____
_____
_____
_____
_____
_____

     Fundamental Accounting Principles, 16ce, Working Papers

DATE	ASSETS					=	LIABILITIES	+	EQUITY	
	CASH	+ ACCOUNTS RECEIVABLE	+ OFFICE SUPPLIES	+ OFFICE EQUIPMENT	+ ELECTRICAL EQUIPMENT	=	ACCOUNTS PAYABLE	+	LARRY POWER, CAPITAL	EXPLANATION OF EQUITY TRANSACTION

Name: _____

Problem 1-9A (Concluded)

Analysis component:

_____
_____
_____
_____
_____
_____

Problem 1-10A

Income Statement		

Statement of Changes in Equity		

Problem 1-10A (Concluded)

	Balance Sheet		

Analysis component:

_____
_____
_____
_____
_____
_____

Problem 1-11A

	TRANSACTION	BALANCE SHEET			INCOME STATEMENT
		TOTAL ASSETS	TOTAL LIABILITIES	EQUITY	PROFIT
1.	Owner invests cash				
2.	Sell services for cash				
3.	Acquire services on credit				
4.	Pay wages with cash				
5.	Owner withdraws cash				
6.	Borrow cash with note payable				
7.	Sell services on credit				
8.	Buy office equipment for cash				
9.	Collect receivable from (7)				
10.	Buy asset with note payable				

Name: _____

Problem 1-1B

a. _____

_____

b. _____

_____

Problem 1-2B

EMAIL

To: _____

From: _____

Subject: _____

_____

_____

_____

_____

_____

_____

_____

_____

_____

_____

_____

_____

_____

_____

_____

_____

_____

_____

_____

_____

_____

_____

_____

_____

_____

_____

_____

_____

_____

_____

Name: _____

Problem 1-3B

2019 Profit (Loss) = [   ]

Supporting Calculations: _____

_____

_____

_____

_____

_____

_____

_____

_____

_____

_____

Problem 1-4B

_____

Income Statement		

Name: _____

Problem 1-4B (Concluded)

Statement of Changes in Equity

Balance Sheet

Analysis component:

_____
_____
_____
_____
_____
_____

Problem 1-5B

Income Statement

Problem 1-5B (Concluded)

Statement of Changes in Equity		

Balance Sheet			

Analysis component:

_____

_____

_____

_____

_____

Problem 1-6B   Part 1

Balance Sheet

Balance Sheet

Name: _____

Problem 1-6B (Concluded)

Part 2

Profit (Loss) Calculation: _____
_____
_____
_____
_____
_____
_____
_____
_____
_____
_____
_____

Analysis component:
_____
_____
_____
_____
_____
_____
_____

Problem 1-7B

Part 1: Company V

(a) _____
_____
_____
_____
_____

(b) _____
_____
_____
_____

(c) _____
_____
_____
_____
_____

Fundamental Accounting Principles, 16ce, Working Papers

Name: _____

Problem 1-7B (Continued)

Part 2: Company W

(a) _____
_____
_____
_____

(b) _____
_____
_____
_____
_____
_____
_____
_____

(c) _____
_____
_____
_____
_____
_____
_____
_____

Part 3: Company X

_____
_____
_____
_____
_____
_____
_____
_____
_____
_____
_____
_____
_____
_____

Name: _____

Problem 1 7B (Concluded)

Part 4: Company Y

_____
_____
_____
_____
_____
_____
_____
_____
_____
_____
_____
_____
_____
_____
_____
_____
_____
_____
_____
_____
_____
_____

Part 5: Company Z

_____
_____
_____
_____
_____
_____
_____
_____
_____
_____
_____
_____
_____
_____
_____
_____
_____
_____
_____
_____
_____

Problem 1-8B (Parts 1 and 2)

CASH	+ ACCOUNTS RECEIVABLE	+ OFFICE SUPPLIES	+ OFFICE EQUIPMENT	+ BUILDING	= ACCOUNTS PAYABLE	+ NOTES PAYABLE	+ LILY ZHANG, CAPITAL	EXPLANATION OF EQUITY TRANSACTION
					ASSETS	= LIABILITIES	+	EQUITY
(a)								
(b)								
Bal.								
(c)								
Bal.								
(d)								
Bal.								
(e)								
Bal.								
(f)								
Bal.								
(g)								
Bal.								
(h)								
Bal.								
(i)								
Bal.								
(j)								
Bal.								
(k)								
Bal.								
(l)								
Bal.								

Name: _____

Problem 1 8B (Concluded)

Part 3

Zhang Consulting
Income Statement
For Year Ended December 31, 2020

Revenues:
   Consulting services revenue ....
Operating expenses:
   Wages expense ....
   Advertising expense ....   _____
      Total operating expenses ....   _____
Profit ....   _____

Zhang Consulting
Statement of Changes in Equity
For Year Ended December 31, 2020

Lily Zhang, capital, January 1
Add: Investments by owner
Profit   _____ _____
   Total
Less: Withdrawals by owner   _____
Lily Zhang, capital, December 31   _____ _____

Zhang Consulting
Balance Sheet
December 31, 2020

Assets		Liabilities	
Cash		Accounts payable	
Accounts receivable		Notes payable	_____
Office supplies		Total liabilities	
Office equipment			
Building			
		Equity	
		Lily Zhang, capital	
Total assets	_____	Total liabilities and equity	_____

Analysis component:

_____
_____
_____
_____
_____
_____
_____
_____
_____

Fundamental Accounting Principles, 16ce, Working Papers

Problem 1-9B

ASSETS					=	LIABILITIES	+	EQUITY	
DATE	CASH	+ ACCOUNTS RECEIVABLE	+ OFFICE SUPPLIES	+ EVENT EQUIPMENT	+ SOUND SYSTEM EQUIPMENT	= ACCOUNTS PAYABLE	+	MICHAEL CANTU, CAPITAL	EXPLANATION OF EQUITY TRANSACTION

Name: _____

Problem 1-9B (Concluded)

Analysis component: _____
_____
_____
_____
_____
_____
_____
_____

Problem 1-10B

Income Statement		

Problem 1-10B (Concluded)

Statement of Changes in Equity

Balance Sheet

Analysis component:

_____

_____

_____

_____

_____

_____

_____

Problem 1-11B

	TRANSACTION	BALANCE SHEET			INCOME STATEMENT
		TOTAL ASSETS	TOTAL LIABILITIES	EQUITY	PROFIT
1.	Owner invests cash				
2.	Pay wages with cash				
3.	Acquire services on credit				
4.	Buy store equipment for cash				
5.	Borrow cash with note payable				
6.	Sell services for cash				
7.	Sell services on credit				
8.	Pay rent with cash				
9.	Owner withdraws cash				
10.	Collect receivable from (7)				

Chapter 2

Quick Study 2-1

1. __A__ Buildings
2. __E__ Building Repair Expense
3. __E__ Wages Expense
4. __L__ Wages Payable
5. __A__ Notes Receivable
6. __L__ Notes Payable
7. __A__ Prepaid Advertising
8. __E__ Advertising Expense
9. __L__ Advertising Payable
10. __L__ Unearned Advertising
11. __R__ Advertising Revenue
12. __R__ Interest Income
13. __E__ Interest Expense
14. __L__ Interest Payable
15. __R__ Subscription Revenue

16. __L__ Unearned Subscription Revenue
17. __A__ Prepaid Subscription Fees
18. __A__ Supplies
19. __E__ Supplies Expense
20. __R__ Rent Revenue
21. __L__ Unearned Rent Revenue
22. __A__ Prepaid Rent
23. __L__ Rent Payable
24. __R__ Service Revenue
25. __OW__ Jessica Vuong, Withdrawals
26. __OE__ Jessica Vuong, Capital
27. __E__ Salaries Expense
28. __L__ Salaries Payable
29. __A__ Furniture
30. __A__ Equipment

Chapter 2

Quick Study 2-2

a.	D	Equipment	i.	C	Notes Receivable
b.	D	Land	j.		Notes Payable
c.	D	Amrit Sandhu, Withdrawals	k.		Amrit Sandhu, Capital
d.	D	Rent Expense	l.	C	Rent Revenue
e.	C	Interest Income	m.	C	Rent Payable
f.	D	Prepaid Rent	n.	D	Interest Expense
g.	D	Accounts Receivable	o.	C	Interest Payable
h.	D	Office Supplies			

Quick Study 2-3

a.	C	To increase Notes Payable	i.	D	To increase Store Equip.
b.	C	To decrease Accounts Rec'ble.	j.	D	To increase Owner, With.
c.		To increase Owner, Capital	k.	C	To decrease Rent Payable
d.	D	To decrease Unearned Revenue	l.	D	To decrease Prepaid Rent
e.	C	To decrease Prepaid Insurance	m.	D	To increase Supplies
f.	C	To decrease Cash	n.	D	To increase Supplies Exp.
g.	D	To increase Utilities Expense	o.	D	To decrease Accts. Payable
h.	C	To increase Revenue			

Quick Study 2-4

a.		Buildings	i.		Office Supplies
b.		Interest Income	j.		Repair Services Revenue
c.		Bob Norton, Withdrawals	k.		Interest Expense
d.		Bob Norton, Capital	l.		Unearned Revenue
e.		Prepaid Insurance	m.		Salaries Payable
f.		Interest Payable	n.		Furniture
g.		Accounts Receivable	o.		Interest Receivable
h.		Salaries Expense			

Quick Study 2-5

a.	A #1	Buildings	i.		Office Supplies
b.	R #4	Interest Income	j.		Repair Services Revenue
c.		Matthew Lee, Withdrawals	k.		Interest Expense
d.		Matthew Lee, Capital	l.	L #2	Unearned Revenue
e.		Prepaid Insurance	m.		Salaries Payable
f.		Interest Payable	n.		Furniture
g.		Accounts Receivable	o.		Interest Receivable
h.	E #6	Salaries Expense			

Fundamental Accounting Principles, 16ce, Working Papers

Quick Study 2-6

a.	Analysis	
	Journal entry analysis	
b.	Analysis	
	Journal entry analysis	
c.	Analysis	
	Journal entry analysis	
d.	Analysis	
	Journal entry analysis	
e.	Analysis	
	Journal entry analysis	

Name: _____

Quick Study 2-7

	Date	Account Titles		Debit	Credit
a.					
b.					
c.					
d.					
e.					

Name: _____

Quick Study 2-8

Part 1 and 2

Cash			Accounts Receivable	
Jul 31	25,000		Jul 31	3,200

Furniture			Accounts Payable	
Jul 31	5,000		500	Jul 31

Douglas Malone, Capital			Revenue	
	28,000	Jul. 31	4,500	Jul. 31

Cleaning Expense	
Jul. 31	1,500

Part 3

_____

_____

_____

_____

Name: _____

Quick Study 2-9

May 2	Analysis	
	Journal entry analysis	
	Journal Entry	

	Date	Account Titles and Explanation		Debit	Credit

May 10	Analysis	
	Journal entry analysis	
	Journal Entry	

	Date	Account Titles and Explanation		Debit	Credit

May 12	Analysis	
	Journal entry analysis	
	Journal Entry	

	Date	Account Titles and Explanation		Debit	Credit

Name: _____

Quick Study 2-9 (cont'd.)

May 15	Analysis				
	Journal entry analysis				
	Journal Entry				
	Date	**Account Titles and Explanation**		**Debit**	**Credit**

May 16	Analysis				
	Journal entry analysis				
	Journal Entry				
	Date	**Account Titles and Explanation**		**Debit**	**Credit**

May 22	Analysis				
	Journal entry analysis				
	Journal Entry				
	Date	**Account Titles and Explanation**		**Debit**	**Credit**

Name: _____

Quick Study 2-10

Parts 1 and 2

Cash				
Apr. 30	15,000			

Accounts Receivable				
Apr. 30	3,200			

Car				

Accounts Payable				
		6,000	Apr. 30	

Unearned Revenue				
		1,800	Apr. 30	

Dee Bell, Capital				
		8,900	Apr. 30	

Revenue				
		3,000	Apr. 30	

Wages Expense				
Apr. 30	1,500			

Part 3

_____

_____

_____

_____

Fundamental Accounting Principles, 16ce, Working Papers

Name: _____

Quick Study 2-11

Accounts Receivable	
1,000	650
400	920
920	1,500
3,000	
5320	3070
2250	

Accounts Payable	
250	250
900	1,800
650	1,400
	650
1800	4100
	2300

Service Revenue	
	13,000
	2,500
	810
	3,500
	19810

Utilities Expense	
610	
520	
390	
275	
1795	

Cash	
3,900	2,400
17,800	3,900
14,500	21,800
340	
36540	28100
8440	

Notes Payable	
4,000	50,000
8,000	
12000	50 000
	38000

Quick Study 2-12

GENERAL JOURNAL   Page____

Date	Account Titles and Explanation	PR	Debit	Credit
May 1	Equitment		500	
	accounts payable			500
	Purchased equipment on account			
May 2	accounts payable		500	
	cash			500
	Paid for equitment May 1			
3	Suplies		100	
	Cash			100
	Purchased suplies for cash			
4	Wage exspense		2000	
	cash			2000
	Paid wages to employees			
5	cash		750	
	Service revenue			750
	Performed service revenue for client			
6	accounts recvible		2500	
	Service revenue			2500
	did work for customer on credit			
7	cash		2500	
	accounts recvible			2500
	colleted May 6 customer account			

Quick Study 2-13

GENERAL JOURNAL

Page_____

Date	Account Titles and Explanation	PR	Debit	Credit
Jan 3	Cash		60,000	
	Equitment		40,000	
	Stan Adams, capital			100,000
	Investment by Owner			
Jan 4	Office Supples		340	
	Accounts Payable			340
	Purchased office supplies on credit			
Jan 6	Cash		5200	
	Landscaping service revenue			5200
	Purchased office supplies on credit			
Jan 15	Accounts payable		200	
	Cash			200
	Paid part of the Jan 4 credit purchase			
Jan 16	Office Supplies		700	
	Accounts payable			700
	Purchased office Supplies on account			
Jan 30	accounts payable			
	Cash		140	
	Paid the balance owing re Jan 4 credit			140
	Purchase; 340 - 200 paid on Jan 15 = 140			

Name: _____

Quick Study 2-14

Cash   ACCOUNT NO. ____

DATE	EXPLANATION	PR	DEBIT	CREDIT	BALANCE

Office Supplies   ACCOUNT NO. ____

DATE	EXPLANATION	PR	DEBIT	CREDIT	BALANCE

Equipment   ACCOUNT NO. ____

DATE	EXPLANATION	PR	DEBIT	CREDIT	BALANCE

Accounts Payable   ACCOUNT NO. ____

DATE	EXPLANATION	PR	DEBIT	CREDIT	BALANCE

Stan Adams, Capital   ACCOUNT NO. ____

DATE	EXPLANATION	PR	DEBIT	CREDIT	BALANCE

Landscaping Services Revenue   ACCOUNT NO. ____

DATE	EXPLANATION	PR	DEBIT	CREDIT	BALANCE

Fundamental Accounting Principles, 16ce, Working Papers

Name: _____

Quick Study 2-15

Trial Balance		
	Debit	**Credit**

Quick Study 2-16

Quick Study 2-17

Quick Study 2-18

Name: _____

Exercise 2-1

		(a) Basic Account	(b) Financial Statement	(c) Normal Balance	(d) Effect of a Debit	(e) Effect of a Credit
a.	Cash					
b.	Supplies					
c.	Accounts Payable					
d.	Yoojin Chang, Capital Account					
e.	Yoojin Chang, Withdrawals					
f.	Design Revenue					
g.	Salaries Expense					
h.	Accounts Receivable					
i.	Notes Payable					
j.	Prepaid insurance					

Fundamental Accounting Principles, 16ce, Working Papers

Name: _____

Exercise 2-2

a.	**Analysis**	
	Journal entry analysis	
b.	**Analysis**	
	Journal entry analysis	
c.	**Analysis**	
	Journal entry analysis	
d.	**Analysis**	
	Journal entry analysis	
e.	**Analysis**	
	Journal entry analysis	
f.	**Analysis**	
	Journal entry analysis	
g.	**Analysis**	
	Journal entry analysis	

Name: _____

Exercise 2-3

	Date	Account Titles and Explanation		Debit	Credit
a.					
b.					
c.					
d.					
e.					
f.					
g.					

Fundamental Accounting Principles, 16ce, Working Papers

Name: _____

Exercise 2-4

Parts 1 and 2

Cash	101

Accounts Receivable	106

Equipment	161

Accounts Payable	201

Christina Reis, Capital	301

Revenue	403

3.

_____

_____

_____

_____

_____

_____

Name: _____

Exercise 2-5

a.	Analysis	

	Journal entry analysis	

	Journal Entry				
	Date	**Account Titles and Explanation**		**Debit**	**Credit**

b.	Analysis	

	Journal entry analysis	

	Journal Entry				
	Date	**Account Titles and Explanation**		**Debit**	**Credit**

c.	Analysis	

	Journal entry analysis	

	Journal Entry				
	Date	**Account Titles and Explanation**		**Debit**	**Credit**

Exercise 2-5 (cont'd.)

d.	Analysis	
	Journal entry analysis	
	Journal Entry	

Date	Account Titles and Explanation		Debit	Credit

e.	Analysis	
	Journal entry analysis	
	Journal Entry	

Date	Account Titles and Explanation		Debit	Credit

f.	Analysis	
	Journal entry analysis	
	Journal Entry	

Date	Account Titles and Explanation		Debit	Credit

Exercise 2-5 (concl'd.)

g.	Analysis	
	Journal entry analysis	
	Journal Entry	

	Date	Account Titles and Explanation		Debit	Credit

h.	Analysis	
	Journal entry analysis	
	Journal Entry	

	Date	Account Titles and Explanation		Debit	Credit

i.	Analysis	
	Journal entry analysis	
	Journal Entry	

	Date	Account Titles and Explanation		Debit	Credit

Name: _____

Exercise 2-6

Cash

Accounts Payable

William Curtis, Capital

Accounts Receivable

William Curtis, Withdrawals

Office Supplies

Revenue

Office Equipment

Rent Expense

Name: _____

Exercise 2-7

GENERAL JOURNAL

Page____

Trans.	Account Titles and Explanation	PR	Debit	Credit

Transactions not creating revenue and the reasons:

_____
_____
_____
_____
_____
_____
_____
_____
_____
_____
_____
_____

Exercise 2-8

GENERAL JOURNAL

Page____

Date	Account Titles and Explanation	PR	Debit	Credit

Name: _____

Exercise 2-8 (concl'd.)

Transactions not creating revenue and the reasons:

_____
_____
_____
_____
_____
_____
_____
_____
_____
_____
_____
_____
_____
_____
_____
_____

Exercise 2-9

Parts 1 and 3

Note: T-accounts may be used or the balance column format; both are provided for in Parts 1 and 3 of this exercise.

Cash	101		Accounts Receivable	106
			Equipment	150
Accounts Payable	201		Manny Gill, Capital	301
Manny Gill, Withdrawals	302		Revenue	401
			Expenses	501

Name: _____

Exercise 2-9 (cont'd.)

Note: T-accounts may be used or the balance column format; both are provided for in Parts 1 and 3 of this exercise.

GENERAL LEDGER

Cash   ACCOUNT NO. 101

DATE	EXPLANATION	PR	DEBIT	CREDIT	BALANCE

Accounts Receivable   ACCOUNT NO. 106

DATE	EXPLANATION	PR	DEBIT	CREDIT	BALANCE

Equipment   ACCOUNT NO. 150

DATE	EXPLANATION	PR	DEBIT	CREDIT	BALANCE

Accounts Payable   ACCOUNT NO. 201

DATE	EXPLANATION	PR	DEBIT	CREDIT	BALANCE

Manny Gill, Capital   ACCOUNT NO. 301

DATE	EXPLANATION	PR	DEBIT	CREDIT	BALANCE

Manny Gill, Withdrawals   ACCOUNT NO. 302

DATE	EXPLANATION	PR	DEBIT	CREDIT	BALANCE

Exercise 2-9 (cont'd.)

	Revenue				ACCOUNT NO. 401
DATE	**EXPLANATION**	**PR**	**DEBIT**	**CREDIT**	**BALANCE**

	Expenses				ACCOUNT NO. 501
DATE	**EXPLANATION**	**PR**	**DEBIT**	**CREDIT**	**BALANCE**

Part 2

	GENERAL JOURNAL			Page_____
Date	**Account Titles and Explanation**	**PR**	**Debit**	**Credit**

Exercise 2-9 (cont'd.)

	GENERAL JOURNAL			Page____

Date	Account Titles and Explanation	PR	Debit	Credit

Part 4

West Secure
Trial Balance
July 31, 2020

Acct. No.	Account Title	Debit	Credit

Part 5

West Secure
Income Statement
For Month Ended July 31, 2020

Revenue			
Expenses			
Profit			

Name: _____

Exercise 2-9 (concl'd.)

West Secure

Statement of Changes in Equity		
For Month Ended July 31, 2020		
Manny Gill, capital, July 1		
Add: Investments by owner		
Profit		
Total		
Less: Withdrawals by owner		
Manny Gill, capital, July 31		

West Secure

Balance Sheet			
July 31, 2020			
Assets		Liabilities	
Cash		Accounts payable	
Accounts receivable		Equity	
Equipment		Manny Gill, capital	
Total assets		Total liabilities and equity	

Analysis component:

_____
_____
_____
_____
_____
_____
_____
_____
_____
_____
_____

Name: _____

Exercise 2-10

Account Number	Account Name	Account Number	Account Name
_____	Cash	_____	Aaron Paquette, Withdrawals
_____	Accounts Receivable	_____	Consulting Revenues
_____	Office Equipment	_____	Salaries Expense
_____	Accounts Payable	_____	Rent Expense
_____	Unearned Revenue	_____	Utilities Expense
_____	Aaron Paquette, Capital		

Exercise 2-11 Part 1

GENERAL JOURNAL

Page____

Date	Account Titles and Explanation	PR	Debit	Credit

Name: _____

Exercise 2-11 (cont'd.)

Part 2

Cash		101
Bal.	15,000	

Accounts Receivable		115
Bal.	3,800	

Office Equipment		160
Bal.	22,500	

Accounts Payable		210
	8,000	Bal.

Unearned Revenue		215
	2,600	Bal.

Aaron Paquette, Capital		310
	9,500	Bal.

Aaron Paquette, Withdrawals		320
Bal.	2,000	

Consulting Revenues		410
	41,700	Bal.

Salaries Expense		510
Bal.	10,000	

Rent Expense		520
Bal.	7,500	

Utilities Expense		530
Bal.	1,000	

Name: _____

Exercise 2-11 (cont'd.)

Part 3

Trial Balance		

Part 4

Income Statement		

Name: _____

Exercise 2-11 (concl'd.)

Part 5

Statement of Changes in Equity		

Part 6

Balance Sheet			

Analysis component:

_____
_____
_____
_____
_____
_____
_____
_____
_____
_____
_____

Name: _____

Exercise 2-12

GENERAL JOURNAL				Page_____

Date		Account Titles and Explanation	PR	Debit	Credit
a.					
b.					
c.					
d.					
e.					
f.					
g.					

Name: _____

Exercise 2-13

GENERAL JOURNAL

Page_____

Date		Account Titles and Explanation	PR	Debit	Credit

Name: _____

Exercise 2-14

GENERAL LEDGER

Cash — ACCOUNT NO. 101

DATE	EXPLANATION	PR	DEBIT	CREDIT	BALANCE
2019					
Dec. 31	Beginning balance				850

Accounts Receivable — ACCOUNT NO. 106

DATE	EXPLANATION	PR	DEBIT	CREDIT	BALANCE
2019					
Dec. 31	Beginning balance				300

Equipment — ACCOUNT NO. 167

DATE	EXPLANATION	PR	DEBIT	CREDIT	BALANCE
2019					
Dec. 31	Beginning balance				1,500

Accounts Payable — ACCOUNT NO. 201

DATE	EXPLANATION	PR	DEBIT	CREDIT	BALANCE
2019					
Dec. 31	Beginning balance				325

Toshi Sato, Capital — ACCOUNT NO. 301

DATE	EXPLANATION	PR	DEBIT	CREDIT	BALANCE
2019					
Dec. 31	Beginning balance				2,325

Name: _____

Exercise 2-14 (concl'd.)

Toshi Sato, Withdrawals — ACCOUNT NO. 302

DATE	EXPLANATION	PR	DEBIT	CREDIT	BALANCE
2019					
Dec. 31	Beginning balance				300

Revenue — ACCOUNT NO. 401

DATE	EXPLANATION	PR	DEBIT	CREDIT	BALANCE
2019					
Dec. 31	Beginning balance				1,800

Salaries Expense — ACCOUNT NO. 622

DATE	EXPLANATION	PR	DEBIT	CREDIT	BALANCE
2019					
Dec. 31	Beginning balance				1,500

Analysis component:

_____
_____
_____
_____
_____
_____
_____
_____
_____
_____
_____
_____

Exercise 2-15

GENERAL JOURNAL   Page____

Date		Account Titles and Explanation	PR	Debit	Credit

Cash   ACCOUNT NO. 101

DATE	EXPLANATION	PR	DEBIT	CREDIT	BALANCE

Office Supplies   ACCOUNT NO. 124

DATE	EXPLANATION	PR	DEBIT	CREDIT	BALANCE

Prepaid Rent   ACCOUNT NO. 131

DATE	EXPLANATION	PR	DEBIT	CREDIT	BALANCE

Photography Equipment   ACCOUNT NO. 167

DATE	EXPLANATION	PR	DEBIT	CREDIT	BALANCE

Joseph Eagle, Capital   ACCOUNT NO. 301

DATE	EXPLANATION	PR	DEBIT	CREDIT	BALANCE

Photography Revenue   ACCOUNT NO. 401

DATE	EXPLANATION	PR	DEBIT	CREDIT	BALANCE

Utilities Expense   ACCOUNT NO. 690

DATE	EXPLANATION	PR	DEBIT	CREDIT	BALANCE

Name: _____

Exercise 2-16 (concl'd.)

Trial Balance

	Debit	Credit

Analysis component:

_____

_____

_____

_____

_____

_____

_____

_____

_____

_____

_____

Name: _____

Exercise 2-17

Cash	101		Office Supplies	124

Photography Equipment	167

Prepaid Rent	131		Photography Revenue	401

Joseph Eagle, Capital	301		Utilities Expense	690

Trial Balance

	Debit	Credit

Analysis component:

_____
_____
_____
_____
_____
_____
_____
_____

Name: _____

Exercise 2-18

Income Statement

Statement of Changes in Equity

Balance Sheet

Analysis component:

_____
_____
_____
_____
_____
_____
_____

Fundamental Accounting Principles, 16ce, Working Papers

Name: _____

Exercise 2-19

Income Statement

Statement of Changes in Equity

Balance Sheet

Name: _____

Exercise 2-20

Income Statement

Statement of Changes in Equity

Balance Sheet

Chapter 2

Name: _____

Exercise 2-21

Description	(1) Difference Between Debit and Credit Column	(2) Column With the Larger Total	(3) Identify Account(s) Incorrectly Stated	(4) Amount That Account(s) is Overstated or Understated
a. A $2,400 debit to Rent Expense was posted as a $1,590 debit.	$810	Credit	Rent Expense	Rent Expense is understated by $810
b. A $42,000 debit to Machinery was posted as a debit to Accounts Payable.				
c. A $4,950 credit to Services Revenue was posted as a $495 credit.				
d. A $1,440 debit to Store Supplies was not posted at all.				
e. A $2,250 debit to Prepaid Insurance was posted as a debit to Insurance Expense.				
f. A $4,050 credit to Cash was posted twice as two credits to the Cash account.				
g. A $9,900 debit to the owner's withdrawals account was debited to the owner's capital account.				

Exercise 2-22

a. _____

b. _____

c. _____

d. _____

e. _____

Name: _____

Exercise 2-23

Case A: _____
_____
_____
_____
_____
_____
_____
_____
_____
_____
_____

Case B: _____
_____
_____
_____
_____
_____
_____
_____
_____
_____
_____

Case C: _____
_____
_____
_____
_____
_____
_____
_____
_____
_____
_____
_____

Name: _____

Problem 2-1A

Nov 1	Analysis				
	Journal entry analysis				
	Journal Entry				
	Date	**Account Titles and Explanation**		**Debit**	**Credit**
Nov 3	Analysis				
	Journal entry analysis				
	Journal Entry				
	Date	**Account Titles and Explanation**		**Debit**	**Credit**

Problem 2-1A (cont'd.)

Nov 7	Analysis				
	Journal entry analysis				
	Journal Entry				
	Date	**Account Titles and Explanation**		**Debit**	**Credit**
Nov 9	Analysis				
	Journal entry analysis				
	Journal Entry				
	Date	**Account Titles and Explanation**		**Debit**	**Credit**
Nov 13	Analysis				
	Journal entry analysis				
	Journal Entry				
	Date	**Account Titles and Explanation**		**Debit**	**Credit**

Problem 2-1A (cont'd.)

Nov 17	Analysis				
	Journal entry analysis				
	Journal Entry				
	Date	**Account Titles and Explanation**		**Debit**	**Credit**

Nov 21	Analysis				
	Journal entry analysis				
	Journal Entry				
	Date	**Account Titles and Explanation**		**Debit**	**Credit**

Nov 23	Analysis				
	Journal entry analysis				
	Journal Entry				
	Date	**Account Titles and Explanation**		**Debit**	**Credit**

Problem 2-1A (concl'd.)

Nov 27	Analysis				
	Journal entry analysis				
	Journal Entry				
	Date	**Account Titles and Explanation**		**Debit**	**Credit**
Nov 30	Analysis				
	Journal entry analysis				
	Journal Entry				
	Date	**Account Titles and Explanation**		**Debit**	**Credit**

Problem 2-2A Parts 1 and 2

Cash

Land

Accounts Payable

Long-Term Notes Payable

Name: _____

Problem 2-2A (concl'd.)

Accounts Receivable
_____

Tobias Eaden, Capital
_____

Supplies
_____

Tobias Eaden, Withdrawals
_____

Airplane
_____

Revenue
_____

Aircraft Equipment
_____

Wages Expense
_____

Building
_____

Part 3

_____
_____
_____
_____

Name: _____

Problem 2-3A

GENERAL JOURNAL

Page____

Date		Account Titles and Explanation	PR	Debit	Credit

Name: _____

Problem 2-3A (concl'd.)

GENERAL JOURNAL   Page____

Date	Account Titles and Explanation	PR	Debit	Credit

Problem 2-4A

GENERAL JOURNAL   Page____

Date	Account Titles and Explanation	PR	Debit	Credit

Name: _____

Problem 2-4A (concl'd.)

GENERAL JOURNAL   Page____

Date	Account Titles and Explanation	PR	Debit	Credit

Problem 2-5A   Parts 1 and 2

GENERAL LEDGER

Cash   ACCOUNT NO. 101

DATE	EXPLANATION	PR	DEBIT	CREDIT	BALANCE

Accounts Receivable   ACCOUNT NO. 106

DATE	EXPLANATION	PR	DEBIT	CREDIT	BALANCE

Office Supplies   ACCOUNT NO. 124

DATE	EXPLANATION	PR	DEBIT	CREDIT	BALANCE

Prepaid Insurance   ACCOUNT NO. 128

DATE	EXPLANATION	PR	DEBIT	CREDIT	BALANCE

Prepaid Rent   ACCOUNT NO. 131

DATE	EXPLANATION	PR	DEBIT	CREDIT	BALANCE

Office Equipment   ACCOUNT NO. 163

DATE	EXPLANATION	PR	DEBIT	CREDIT	BALANCE

Accounts Payable   ACCOUNT NO. 201

DATE	EXPLANATION	PR	DEBIT	CREDIT	BALANCE

Abe Factor, Capital   ACCOUNT NO. 301

DATE	EXPLANATION	PR	DEBIT	CREDIT	BALANCE

Abe Factor, Withdrawals   ACCOUNT NO. 302

DATE	EXPLANATION	PR	DEBIT	CREDIT	BALANCE

Problem 2-5A (concl'd.)

Accounting Revenue   ACCOUNT NO. 401

DATE	EXPLANATION	PR	DEBIT	CREDIT	BALANCE

Utilities Expense   ACCOUNT NO. 690

DATE	EXPLANATION	PR	DEBIT	CREDIT	BALANCE

Part 3

Trial Balance

Name: _____

Problem 2-6A

Income Statement

Statement of Changes in Equity

Balance Sheet

Name: _____

Problem 2-7A

GENERAL JOURNAL

Page____

Date		Account Titles and Explanation	PR	Debit	Credit

Name: _____

Problem 2-7A (cont'd.)

GENERAL JOURNAL

Page_____

Date	Account Titles and Explanation	PR	Debit	Credit

Name: _____

Problem 2-7A (cont'd.)

Parts 2 and 3

GENERAL LEDGER

Cash   **ACCOUNT NO. 101**

DATE	EXPLANATION	PR	DEBIT	CREDIT	BALANCE

Accounts Receivable   **ACCOUNT NO. 106**

DATE	EXPLANATION	PR	DEBIT	CREDIT	BALANCE

Office Supplies   **ACCOUNT NO. 124**

DATE	EXPLANATION	PR	DEBIT	CREDIT	BALANCE

Prepaid Insurance   **ACCOUNT NO. 128**

DATE	EXPLANATION	PR	DEBIT	CREDIT	BALANCE

Prepaid Rent   **ACCOUNT NO. 131**

DATE	EXPLANATION	PR	DEBIT	CREDIT	BALANCE

Office Equipment   **ACCOUNT NO. 163**

DATE	EXPLANATION	PR	DEBIT	CREDIT	BALANCE

Name: _____

Problem 2-7A (cont'd.)

Accounts Payable ACCOUNT NO. 201

DATE	EXPLANATION	PR	DEBIT	CREDIT	BALANCE

Elizabeth Wong, Capital ACCOUNT NO. 301

DATE	EXPLANATION	PR	DEBIT	CREDIT	BALANCE

Elizabeth Wong, Withdrawals ACCOUNT NO. 302

DATE	EXPLANATION	PR	DEBIT	CREDIT	BALANCE

Services Revenue ACCOUNT NO. 403

DATE	EXPLANATION	PR	DEBIT	CREDIT	BALANCE

Wages Expense ACCOUNT NO. 623

DATE	EXPLANATION	PR	DEBIT	CREDIT	BALANCE

Utilities Expense ACCOUNT NO. 690

DATE	EXPLANATION	PR	DEBIT	CREDIT	BALANCE

Name: _____

Problem 2-7A (concl'd.)

Part 4

Trial Balance

Analysis component:

Problem 2-8A

Income Statement

Statement of Changes in Equity

Balance Sheet

Problem 2-9A

Income Statement

Statement of Changes in Equity

Balance Sheet

Name: _____

Problem 2-9A (concl'd.)

Analysis component: **GENERAL JOURNAL** Page____

Date	Account Titles and Explanation	PR	Debit	Credit

Problem 2-10A

Part 1

GENERAL JOURNAL Page____

Date	Account Titles and Explanation	PR	Debit	Credit

Name: _____

Problem 2-10A (cont'd.)

Page_____

Date	Account Titles and Explanation	PR	Debit	Credit

Name: _____

Problem 2-10A (cont'd.)

GENERAL JOURNAL

Page_____

Date	Account Titles and Explanation	PR	Debit	Credit

Parts 2 and 3

GENERAL LEDGER

Cash   ACCOUNT NO. 101

DATE	EXPLANATION	PR	DEBIT	CREDIT	BALANCE
2020					
Jun. 30	Beginning balance				26,000

Name: _____

Problem 2-10A (cont'd.)

Accounts Receivable
ACCOUNT NO. 106

DATE		EXPLANATION	PR	DEBIT	CREDIT	BALANCE
2020						
Jun.	30	Beginning balance				3,000

Prepaid Insurance
ACCOUNT NO. 128

DATE		EXPLANATION	PR	DEBIT	CREDIT	BALANCE
2020						
Jun.	30	Beginning balance				500

Office Equipment
ACCOUNT NO. 163

DATE		EXPLANATION	PR	DEBIT	CREDIT	BALANCE
2020						
Jun.	30	Beginning balance				1,700

Drafting Equipment
ACCOUNT NO. 167

DATE		EXPLANATION	PR	DEBIT	CREDIT	BALANCE
2020						
Jun.	30	Beginning balance				1,200

Building
ACCOUNT NO. 173

DATE		EXPLANATION	PR	DEBIT	CREDIT	BALANCE
2020						
Jun.	30	Beginning balance				42,000

Land
ACCOUNT NO. 183

DATE		EXPLANATION	PR	DEBIT	CREDIT	BALANCE
2020						
Jun.	30	Beginning balance				28,000

Fundamental Accounting Principles, 16ce, Working Papers

Name: _____

Problem 2-10A (cont'd.)

Accounts Payable   ACCOUNT NO. 201

DATE	EXPLANATION	PR	DEBIT	CREDIT	BALANCE
2020					
Jun. 30	Beginning balance				1,740

Long-Term Notes Payable   ACCOUNT NO. 251

DATE	EXPLANATION	PR	DEBIT	CREDIT	BALANCE
2020					
Jun. 30	Beginning balance				24,000

Bob Binbutti, Capital   ACCOUNT NO. 301

DATE	EXPLANATION	PR	DEBIT	CREDIT	BALANCE
2020					
Jun. 30	Beginning balance				54,000

Bob Binbutti, Withdrawals   ACCOUNT NO. 302

DATE	EXPLANATION	PR	DEBIT	CREDIT	BALANCE
2020					
Jun. 30	Beginning balance				1,000

Engineering Revenue   ACCOUNT NO. 401

DATE	EXPLANATION	PR	DEBIT	CREDIT	BALANCE
2020					
Jun. 30	Beginning balance				29,600

Wages Expense   ACCOUNT NO. 623

DATE	EXPLANATION	PR	DEBIT	CREDIT	BALANCE
2020					
Jun. 30	Beginning balance				4,000

Problem 2-10A (concl'd.)

Equipment Rental Expense   ACCOUNT NO. 645

DATE	EXPLANATION	PR	DEBIT	CREDIT	BALANCE
2020					
Jun. 30	Beginning balance				1,000

Advertising Expense   ACCOUNT NO. 655

DATE	EXPLANATION	PR	DEBIT	CREDIT	BALANCE
2020					
Jun. 30	Beginning balance				640

Repairs Expense   ACCOUNT NO. 684

DATE	EXPLANATION	PR	DEBIT	CREDIT	BALANCE
2020					
Jun. 30	Beginning balance				300

Parts 4

Trial Balance

Name: _____

Problem 2-11A

Income Statement

Statement of Changes in Equity

Balance Sheet

Problem 2-12A

Part 1

GENERAL JOURNAL

Name: _____

Page_____

Date		Account Titles and Explanation	PR	Debit	Credit

Problem 2-12A (cont'd.)

Parts 2 and 3

Cash		101
Bal.	6,000	

Supplies		126
Bal.	950	

Equipment		161
Bal.	8,000	

Accounts Payable		201
	1,500	Bal.

Unearned Teaching Revenue		233
	9,800	Bal.

Teaching Revenue		401
	46,000	Bal.

Taylor Smith, Capital		301
	3,000	Bal.

Wages Expense		623
Bal.	26,350	

Rent Expense		640
Bal.	6,000	

Taylor Smith, Withdrawals		302
Bal.	13,000	

Name: _____

Problem 2-12A (cont'd)

Part 4

Trial Balance

Name: _____

Problem 2-12A (concl'd.)

Part 5

Income Statement

Statement of Changes in Equity

Balance Sheet

Chapter 2

Problem 2-13A Part 1

Name: _____

GENERAL JOURNAL

Page____

Date	Account Titles and Explanation	PR	Debit	Credit

Problem 2-13A (cont'd.)

Parts 2 and 3

	Cash	101
Bal.	6,200	

	Supplies	126
Bal.	1,050	

	Equipment	161
Bal.	8,200	

Accounts Payable		201
	1,700	Bal.

Wedding Planning Revenue		401
	46,600	Bal.

Unearned Wedding Planning Rev		233
	10,000	Bal.

	Wages Expense	623
Bal.	26,650	

Ranjeet Gill, Capital		301
	3,200	Bal.

	Rent Expense	640
Bal.	6,200	

	Ranjeet Gill, Withdrawals	302
Bal.	13,200	

Name: _____

Problem 2-13A (cont'd)

Part 4

	Trial Balance		

Name: _____

Problem 2-13A (concl'd.)

Part 5

Income Statement

Statement of Changes in Equity

Balance Sheet

Chapter 2

Name: _____

Problem 2-14A

Income Statement

Statement of Changes in Equity

Balance Sheet

Fundamental Accounting Principles, 16ce, Working Papers

Problem 2-14A (concl'd)

Analysis component:

GENERAL JOURNAL   Page_____

Date		Account Titles and Explanation	PR	Debit	Credit

Problem 2-15A

Trial Balance

Calculations:

_____
_____
_____
_____
_____
_____

Name: _____

Problem 2-1B

June 2	Analysis	
	Journal entry analysis	
	Journal Entry	

	Date	Account Titles and Explanation		Debit	Credit

Jun 4	Analysis	
	Journal entry analysis	
	Journal Entry	

	Date	Account Titles and Explanation		Debit	Credit

Jun 8	Analysis	
	Journal entry analysis	
	Journal Entry	

	Date	Account Titles and Explanation		Debit	Credit

Problem 2-1B (cont'd.)

Jun 10	Analysis				
	Journal entry analysis				
	Journal Entry				
	Date	**Account Titles and Explanation**		**Debit**	**Credit**

Jun 14	Analysis				
	Journal entry analysis				
	Journal Entry				
	Date	**Account Titles and Explanation**		**Debit**	**Credit**

Jun 18	Analysis				
	Journal entry analysis				
	Journal Entry				
	Date	**Account Titles and Explanation**		**Debit**	**Credit**

Problem 2-1B (cont'd.)

Jun 22	Analysis				
	Journal entry analysis				
	Journal Entry				
	Date	**Account Titles and Explanations**		**Debit**	**Credit**

Jun 24	Analysis				
	Journal entry analysis				
	Journal Entry				
	Date	**Account Titles and Explanations**		**Debit**	**Credit**

Jun 28	Analysis				
	Journal entry analysis				
	Journal Entry				
	Date	**Account Titles and Explanations**		**Debit**	**Credit**

Name: _____

Problem 2-1B (concl'd.)

Jun 30	Analysis			
	Journal entry analysis			
	Journal Entry			
	Date	**Account Titles and Explanations**	**Debit**	**Credit**

Chapter 2

Problem 2-2B

Parts 1 and 2

Cash		Land

	Accounts Payable

	Long-Term Notes Payable

Accounts Receivable		Trevor Peters, Capital

Office Supplies		Trevor Peters, Withdrawals

Vehicle		Revenue

Office Equipment		Salaries Expense

Building

Fundamental Accounting Principles, 16ce, Working Papers

Name: _____

Problem 2-2B (concl'd.)

Part 3

_____
_____
_____
_____

Name: _____

Problem 2-3B

GENERAL JOURNAL

Page____

Date	Account Titles and Explanation	PR	Debit	Credit

Name: _____

Problem 2-3B (concl'd.)

GENERAL JOURNAL

Page_____

Date	Account Titles and Explanation	PR	Debit	Credit

Problem 2-4B

GENERAL JOURNAL

Page_____

Date	Account Titles and Explanation	PR	Debit	Credit

Name: _____

Problem 2-4B (concl'd.)

GENERAL JOURNAL

Page_____

Date	Account Titles and Explanation	PR	Debit	Credit

Fundamental Accounting Principles, 16ce, Working Papers

Name: _____

Problem 2-5B

Parts 1 and 2

GENERAL LEDGER

Cash   ACCOUNT NO. 101

DATE	EXPLANATION	PR	DEBIT	CREDIT	BALANCE

Accounts Receivable   ACCOUNT NO. 106

DATE	EXPLANATION	PR	DEBIT	CREDIT	BALANCE

Office Supplies   ACCOUNT NO. 124

DATE	EXPLANATION	PR	DEBIT	CREDIT	BALANCE

Prepaid Insurance   ACCOUNT NO. 128

DATE	EXPLANATION	PR	DEBIT	CREDIT	BALANCE

Prepaid Rent   ACCOUNT NO. 131

DATE	EXPLANATION	PR	DEBIT	CREDIT	BALANCE

Office Equipment   ACCOUNT NO. 163

DATE	EXPLANATION	PR	DEBIT	CREDIT	BALANCE

Name: _____

Problem 2-5B (cont'd.)

Accounts Payable — ACCOUNT NO. 201

DATE	EXPLANATION	PR	DEBIT	CREDIT	BALANCE

Francis Dhami, Capital — ACCOUNT NO. 301

DATE	EXPLANATION	PR	DEBIT	CREDIT	BALANCE

Francis Dhami, Withdrawals — ACCOUNT NO. 302

DATE	EXPLANATION	PR	DEBIT	CREDIT	BALANCE

Accounting Revenue — ACCOUNT NO. 401

DATE	EXPLANATION	PR	DEBIT	CREDIT	BALANCE

Professional Development Expense — ACCOUNT NO. 680

DATE	EXPLANATION	PR	DEBIT	CREDIT	BALANCE

Utilities Expense — ACCOUNT NO. 690

DATE	EXPLANATION	PR	DEBIT	CREDIT	BALANCE

Fundamental Accounting Principles, 16ce, Working Papers

Name: _____

Problem 2-5B (concl'd.)

Part 3

Trial Balance		

Name: _____

Problem 2-6B

Income Statement

Statement of Changes in Equity

Balance Sheet

Fundamental Accounting Principles, 16ce, Working Papers

Problem 2-7B

Part 1

GENERAL JOURNAL

Name: _____

Page_____

Date	Account Titles and Explanation	PR	Debit	Credit

Name: _____

Problem 2-7B (cont'd.)

GENERAL JOURNAL

Page_____

Date		Account Titles and Explanation	PR	Debit	Credit

Parts 2 and 3

GENERAL LEDGER

Cash   ACCOUNT NO. 101

DATE	EXPLANATION	PR	DEBIT	CREDIT	BALANCE

Accounts Receivable   ACCOUNT NO. 106

DATE	EXPLANATION	PR	DEBIT	CREDIT	BALANCE

Problem 2-7B (cont'd.)

Office Supplies   ACCOUNT NO. 124

DATE	EXPLANATION	PR	DEBIT	CREDIT	BALANCE

Prepaid Insurance   ACCOUNT NO. 128

DATE	EXPLANATION	PR	DEBIT	CREDIT	BALANCE

Prepaid Rent   ACCOUNT NO. 131

DATE	EXPLANATION	PR	DEBIT	CREDIT	BALANCE

Office Equipment   ACCOUNT NO. 163

DATE	EXPLANATION	PR	DEBIT	CREDIT	BALANCE

Accounts Payable   ACCOUNT NO. 201

DATE	EXPLANATION	PR	DEBIT	CREDIT	BALANCE

Tait Unger, Capital   ACCOUNT NO. 301

DATE	EXPLANATION	PR	DEBIT	CREDIT	BALANCE

Tait Unger, Withdrawals   ACCOUNT NO. 302

DATE	EXPLANATION	PR	DEBIT	CREDIT	BALANCE

Name: _____

Problem 2-7B (concl'd.)

Service Revenue ACCOUNT NO. 401

DATE	EXPLANATION	PR	DEBIT	CREDIT	BALANCE

Wages Expense ACCOUNT NO. 680

DATE	EXPLANATION	PR	DEBIT	CREDIT	BALANCE

Utilities Expense ACCOUNT NO. 690

DATE	EXPLANATION	PR	DEBIT	CREDIT	BALANCE

Part 4

Trial Balance

Analysis component:

_____
_____
_____
_____
_____
_____
_____

Problem 2-8B

Income Statement

Statement of Changes in Equity

Balance Sheet

Name: _____

Problem 2-9B

Income Statement

Statement of Changes in Equity

Balance Sheet

Name: _____

Problem 2-9B (concl'd.)

Analysis Component:

GENERAL JOURNAL

Page____

Date	Account Titles and Explanation	PR	Debit	Credit

Problem 2-10B   Part 1

GENERAL JOURNAL

Page____

Date	Account Titles and Explanation	PR	Debit	Credit

Problem 2-10B (cont'd.)

GENERAL JOURNAL

Date	Account Titles and Explanation	PR	Debit	Credit

Name: _____

Problem 2-10B (cont'd.)

Parts 2 and 3

GENERAL LEDGER

Cash   ACCOUNT NO. 101

DATE	EXPLANATION	PR	DEBIT	CREDIT	BALANCE
2020					
Jun. 30	Beginning balance				75,000

Accounts Receivable   ACCOUNT NO. 106

DATE	EXPLANATION	PR	DEBIT	CREDIT	BALANCE
2020					
Jun. 30	Beginning balance				950

Prepaid Insurance   ACCOUNT NO. 128

DATE	EXPLANATION	PR	DEBIT	CREDIT	BALANCE
2020					
Jun. 30	Beginning balance				275

Trucks   ACCOUNT NO. 153

DATE	EXPLANATION	PR	DEBIT	CREDIT	BALANCE
2020					
Jun. 30	Beginning balance				20,800

Name: _____

Problem 2-10B (cont'd.)

Office Equipment   ACCOUNT NO. 163

DATE	EXPLANATION	PR	DEBIT	CREDIT	BALANCE
2020					
Jun. 30	Beginning balance				1,200

Building   ACCOUNT NO. 173

DATE	EXPLANATION	PR	DEBIT	CREDIT	BALANCE
2020					
Jun. 30	Beginning balance				0

Land   ACCOUNT NO. 183

DATE	EXPLANATION	PR	DEBIT	CREDIT	BALANCE
2020					
Jun. 30	Beginning balance				0

Accounts Payable   ACCOUNT NO. 201

DATE	EXPLANATION	PR	DEBIT	CREDIT	BALANCE
2020					
Jun. 30	Beginning balance				725

Unearned Revenue   ACCOUNT NO. 233

DATE	EXPLANATION	PR	DEBIT	CREDIT	BALANCE
2020					
Jun. 30	Beginning balance				0

Long-Term Notes Payable   ACCOUNT NO. 251

DATE	EXPLANATION	PR	DEBIT	CREDIT	BALANCE
2020					
Jun. 30	Beginning balance				7,000

Chapter 2

Name: _____

Problem 2-10B (cont'd.)

Brett Wilson, Capital ACCOUNT NO. 301

DATE	EXPLANATION	PR	DEBIT	CREDIT	BALANCE
2020					
Jun. 30	Beginning balance				83,825

Brett Wilson, Withdrawals ACCOUNT NO. 302

DATE	EXPLANATION	PR	DEBIT	CREDIT	BALANCE
2020					
Jun. 30	Beginning balance				600

Revenue ACCOUNT NO. 401

DATE	EXPLANATION	PR	DEBIT	CREDIT	BALANCE
2020					
Jun. 30	Beginning balance				8,400

Wages Expense ACCOUNT NO. 623

DATE	EXPLANATION	PR	DEBIT	CREDIT	BALANCE
2020					
Jun. 30	Beginning balance				780

Truck Rental Expense ACCOUNT NO. 645

DATE	EXPLANATION	PR	DEBIT	CREDIT	BALANCE
2020					
Jun. 30	Beginning balance				230

Advertising Expense ACCOUNT NO. 655

DATE	EXPLANATION	PR	DEBIT	CREDIT	BALANCE
2020					
Jun. 30	Beginning balance				75

Repairs Expense ACCOUNT NO. 684

DATE	EXPLANATION	PR	DEBIT	CREDIT	BALANCE
2020					
Jun. 30	Beginning balance				40

Name: _____

Problem 2-10B (concl'd.)

Part 4

Trial Balance		

Fundamental Accounting Principles, 16ce, Working Papers

Income Statement

Statement of Changes in Equity

Balance Sheet

Name: _____

Problem 2-12B

Part 1

GENERAL JOURNAL

Page_____

Date		Account Titles and Explanation	PR	Debit	Credit

Name: _____

Problem 2-12B (cont'd.)

Parts 2 and 3

Cash			101
Bal.	26,000		

Office Supplies			124
Bal.	900		

Office Equipment			163
Bal.	36,000		

Accounts Payable			201
		43,000	Bal.

Notes Payable			205
		20,000	Bal.

Travel Revenue			401
		34,000	Bal.

Ike Petrov, Capital			301
		8,000	Bal.

Wages Expense			623
Bal.	38,000		

Interest Expense			633
Bal.	100		

Ike Petrov, Withdrawals			302
Bal.	4,000		

Name: _____

Problem 2-12B (cont'd.)

Part 4

Trial Balance		

Name: _____

Problem 2-12B (cont'd.)

Part 5

Income Statement

Statement of Changes in Equity

Balance Sheet

Name: _____

Problem 2-12B (concl'd.)

Analysis component:

_____
_____
_____
_____
_____
_____
_____
_____
_____
_____

Fundamental Accounting Principles, 16ce, Working Papers

Problem 2-13B

Part 1

GENERAL JOURNAL

Page____

Date	Account Titles and Explanation	PR	Debit	Credit

Problem 2-13B (cont'd.)

Name: _____

Parts 2 and 3

	Cash	101
Bal.	17,500	

	Supplies	126
Bal.	1,700	

	Equipment	161
Bal.	9,500	

	Accounts Payable	201
	3,000	Bal.

	Unearned Travel Deposit Revenue	233
	11,300	Bal.

	Travel Planning Revenue	401
	60,500	Bal.

	Tom Keenan, Capital	301
	4,500	Bal.

	Wages Expense	623
Bal.	28,600	

	Rent Expense	640
Bal.	7,500	

	Tom Keenan, Withdrawals	302
Bal.	14,500	

Fundamental Accounting Principles, 16ce, Working Papers

Name: _____

Problem 2-13B (cont'd.)

Part 4

Trial Balance		

Name: _____

	Income Statement		

Name: _____

Problem 2-13B (concl'd.)

Statement of Changes in Equity

Balance Sheet

Analysis component:

_____
_____
_____
_____
_____
_____
_____
_____
_____

Problem 2-14B

Income Statement

Statement of Changes in Equity

Name: _____

Problem 2-14B (concl'd.)

Balance Sheet

Analysis component: _____

_____

_____

_____

_____

_____

_____

_____

_____

Name: _____

Problem 2-15B

Trial Balance		

Calculations:

_____
_____
_____
_____
_____
_____
_____
_____
_____
_____
_____
_____
_____
_____
_____
_____
_____
_____
_____

Fundamental Accounting Principles, 16ce, Working Papers

Name: _____

Cumulative Problem

Echo Systems

Parts 2 and 6: October/November Transactions

GENERAL JOURNAL

Date	Account Titles and Explanation	PR	Debit	Credit

Cumulative Problem

Echo Systems (Cont'd.)

Date	Account Titles and Explanation	PR	Debit	Credit

Name: _____

Cumulative Problem

Echo Systems (Cont'd.)

Date	Account Titles and Explanation	PR	Debit	Credit

Cumulative Problem (cont.)

Parts 1, 3, and 7   **GENERAL LEDGER**

Cash   ACCOUNT NO. 101

DATE	EXPLANATION	PR	DEBIT	CREDIT	BALANCE

Accounts Receivable   ACCOUNT NO. 106

DATE	EXPLANATION	PR	DEBIT	CREDIT	BALANCE

Computer Supplies   ACCOUNT NO. 126

DATE	EXPLANATION	PR	DEBIT	CREDIT	BALANCE

Cumulative Problem (cont'd.)

Prepaid Insurance   ACCOUNT NO. 128

DATE	EXPLANATION	PR	DEBIT	CREDIT	BALANCE

Prepaid Rent   ACCOUNT NO. 131

DATE	EXPLANATION	PR	DEBIT	CREDIT	BALANCE

Office Equipment   ACCOUNT NO. 163

DATE	EXPLANATION	PR	DEBIT	CREDIT	BALANCE

Computer Equipment   ACCOUNT NO. 167

DATE	EXPLANATION	PR	DEBIT	CREDIT	BALANCE

Accounts Payable   ACCOUNT NO. 201

DATE	EXPLANATION	PR	DEBIT	CREDIT	BALANCE

Mary Graham, Capital   ACCOUNT NO. 301

DATE	EXPLANATION	PR	DEBIT	CREDIT	BALANCE

Mary Graham, Withdrawals   ACCOUNT NO. 302

DATE	EXPLANATION	PR	DEBIT	CREDIT	BALANCE

Cumulative Problem (cont'd.)

Computer Services Revenue — ACCOUNT NO. 403

DATE	EXPLANATION	PR	DEBIT	CREDIT	BALANCE

Wages Expense — ACCOUNT NO. 623

DATE	EXPLANATION	PR	DEBIT	CREDIT	BALANCE

Advertising Expense — ACCOUNT NO. 655

DATE	EXPLANATION	PR	DEBIT	CREDIT	BALANCE

Mileage Expense — ACCOUNT NO. 676

DATE	EXPLANATION	PR	DEBIT	CREDIT	BALANCE

Repairs Expense, Computer — ACCOUNT NO. 684

DATE	EXPLANATION	PR	DEBIT	CREDIT	BALANCE

Charitable Donations Expense — ACCOUNT NO. 699

DATE	EXPLANATION	PR	DEBIT	CREDIT	BALANCE

Cumulative Problem (cont'd.)

Part 4

ECHO SYSTEMS
Trial Balance
October 31, 2020

	Debit	Credit

Part 5

ECHO SYSTEMS
Income Statement
Month Ended October 31, 2020

Cumulative Problem (cont'd.)

ECHO SYSTEMS
Statement of Changes in Equity
Month Ended October 31, 2020

ECHO SYSTEMS
Balance Sheet
October 31, 2020

Fundamental Accounting Principles, 16ce, Working Papers

Name: _____

Cumulative Problem (cont'd.)

Part 8

	Debit	Credit
ECHO SYSTEMS		
Trial Balance		
November 30, 2020		

Part 9

ECHO SYSTEMS		
Income Statement		
For Two Months Ended November 30, 2020		

Name: _____

Cumulative Problem (concl'd.)

ECHO SYSTEMS
Statement of Changes in Equity
For Two Months Ended November 30, 2020

ECHO SYSTEMS
Balance Sheet
November 30, 2020

Quick Study 3-1

1.   Timeliness

2.   Matching

3.   Revenue recognition

4.   Matching

Quick Study 3-2

1.   March

2.   every month

Quick Study 3-3

1.   **Cash Basis:**   33 000

          − 24 000   22 500

              9 000   − 2 250

                      + 3 750

         = 9 000   24 000

2.   **Accrual Basis:**

3.   **Difference:**

Name: _____

Quick Study 3-4

a. $\dfrac{12000}{12x} = \$1000$ Monthly

b. 6 months

GENERAL JOURNAL

Page____

Date	Account Titles and Explanation	Debit	Credit
	Prepaid insurance	12000	
c.	Cash		12000
d.	intrest exspense	6000	
	Prepaid insurance		6000

Quick Study 3-5

GENERAL JOURNAL

Page____

Date	Account Titles and Explanation	Debit	Credit
	Suplies	12000	
a.	Credit		12000
b.	Supplies exspens	7000	
	Suplies		7000

c. $5000

Chapter 3   Name: _____

Quick Study 3-6

GENERAL JOURNAL   Page____

Date		Account Titles and Explanation	Debit	Credit
April	1			
a.		Prepaid insurance	7680	
		Cash		7680
		intrest exspense	2880	
		prepaid insurest		2880

b.   9 Months

$\frac{7680}{24} = 320 \times 9 = \$2880$

GENERAL JOURNAL   Page____

Date		Account Titles and Explanation	Debit	Credit
2021				
		insurance exspense	3840	
		prepaid insurance		3840

c. _____

GENERAL JOURNAL   Page____

Date		Account Titles and Explanation	Debit	Credit
2022				
		intrest exspense	960	
		prepaid insurance		960

d.   3 Months

9 Months

+ 12 Months

3 Month = 24 months

7680	7680
	3840
	960

Quick Study 3-7

GENERAL JOURNAL   Page____

Date		Account Titles and Explanation	Debit	Credit
		equipment	12000	
a.		cash		12000

b.   Cost - estamat val end of use _____

_____

c. $\frac{12000 - 2000}{5 \text{ years}} = \frac{2000}{1 \text{ year}}$

_____

_____

GENERAL JOURNAL   Page____

Date		Account Titles and Explanation	Debit	Credit
		Depressiation exspense equit	2000	
d.		accomulaee depreasiation equit		2000

Quick Study 3-8

GENERAL JOURNAL   Page____

Date		Account Titles and Explanation	Debit	Credit
		veihcle	32000	
a.		Cash		32000

Quick Study 3-8 (concl'd.)

b. $\frac{32000 - 8000}{4}$

= 6000/yr × 10/12 = 5000

GENERAL JOURNAL   Page____

Date	Account Titles and Explanation	Debit	Credit
2020 c.	Dep exp vehcle	5000	
	Accum Dep vencile		5000

d. _____

GENERAL JOURNAL   Page____

Date	Account Titles and Explanation	Debit	Credit
e.	Cash	300	
	Unearned rev		300

Quick Study 3-9

GENERAL JOURNAL   Page____

Date	Account Titles and Explanation	Debit	Credit
a.	Cash	300	
	Unearned rev		300
	Unearned revenue	75	
	revenue		75

b. $\frac{300}{12}$ = $25

Quick Study 3-9 (cont'd.)

c.   3 Months _____
_____
_____
_____

GENERAL JOURNAL   Page____

Date	Account Titles and Explanation	PR	Debit	Credit
d.				

Quick Study 3-10

GENERAL JOURNAL   Page____

Date	Account Titles and Explanation	PR	Debit	Credit
a.	Cash		12000	
	Unearned revenue			12000

b.   12,000 - 3000 (unearned) = $9000 (earned)
_____
_____

GENERAL JOURNAL   Page____

Date	Account Titles and Explanation	PR	Debit	Credit
c.	Unearned revenue		4000	
	revenue			4000

Quick Study 3-11

a. _____
   _____
   _____

b. _____
   _____
   _____

GENERAL JOURNAL   Page____

Date	Account Titles and Explanation	PR	Debit	Credit
c.				

Quick Study 3-12

a. _____
   _____
   _____

b. _____
   _____
   _____

GENERAL JOURNAL   Page____

Date	Account Titles and Explanation	PR	Debit	Credit
c.				
d.				

Name: _____

Quick Study 3-13

GENERAL JOURNAL Page____

Date		Account Titles and Explanation	PR	Debit	Credit
a.					
b.					

Quick Study 3-14

a. _____

_____

_____

_____

_____

_____

_____

_____

_____

GENERAL JOURNAL Page____

Date		Account Titles and Explanation	PR	Debit	Credit
b.					
c.					

Chapter 3

Quick Study 3-15

Debits	Credits	
a. _____	_____	Accrual of unpaid and unrecorded advertising that was used by Stark Company.
b. _____	_____	Adjustment of Unearned Services Revenue to recognize earned revenue.
c. _____	_____	Recorded revenue for work completed this accounting period; the cash will be received in the next period.
d. _____	_____	The cost of Equipment was matched to the time periods benefited.
e. _____	_____	Adjustment of Prepaid Advertising to recognize the portion used.

Quick Study 3-16

	Dr./Cr.	Account Titles	Statement
(a)	Debit		
	Credit		
(b)	Debit		
	Credit		
(c)	Debit		
	Credit		
(d)	Debit		
	Credit		
(e)	Debit		
	Credit		

Quick Study 3-17

	Type of Adjustment	Profit will be overstated, understated, or no effect	Assets will be overstated, understated, or no effect	Liabilities will be overstated, understated, or no effect	Equity will be overstated, understated, or no effect
		If adjustment is not recorded:			
a.	Prepaid Expenses				
b.	Depreciation				
c.	Unearned Revenues				
d.	Accrued Expenses				
e.	Accrued Revenues				

Name: _____

Quick Study 3-18

GENERAL JOURNAL

Page____

Date		Account Titles and Explanation	PR	Debit	Credit

*Quick Study 3-19

GENERAL JOURNAL

Page____

Date		Account Titles and Explanation	PR	Debit	Credit

Name: _____

*Quick Study 3-20

GENERAL JOURNAL
Page____

Date		Account Titles and Explanation	PR	Debit	Credit

*Quick Study 3-21

GENERAL JOURNAL
Page____

Date		Account Titles and Explanation	PR	Debit	Credit
a.					
b.					
c.					
d.					

Name: _____

Exercise 3-1

a. _____
_____
_____
_____

b. _____
_____
_____
_____

c. _____
_____
_____
_____

Exercise 3-2

1. _____	7. _____	
2. _____	8. _____	
3. _____	9. _____	
4. _____	10. _____	
5. _____	11. _____	
6. _____	12. _____	

Exercise 3-3

GENERAL JOURNAL   Page____

Date	Account Titles and Explanation	PR	Debit	Credit
a.				

Exercise 3-3 (concl'd.)

Date		Account Titles and Explanation	PR	Debit	Credit
b.					
c.					

Exercise 3-4

Part 1: Calculations

a.

_____

_____

_____

_____

b.

_____

_____

_____

_____

c.

_____

_____

_____

_____

_____

_____

Name: _____

Exercise 3-4 (concl'd.)

Part 1: Adjusting entries

GENERAL JOURNAL

Page____

Date	Account Titles and Explanation	PR	Debit	Credit
a.				
b.				
c.				

2. _____

_____

_____

_____

3. _____

_____

_____

_____

Name: _____

GENERAL JOURNAL

Page_____

Date	Account Titles and Explanation	PR	Debit	Credit
a.				
b.				
c.				

Exercise 3-6

GENERAL JOURNAL   Page____

	Date	Account Titles and Explanation	PR	Debit	Credit
a.					
b.					
c.					

Exercise 3-7

1.

GENERAL JOURNAL   Page____

	Date	Account Titles and Explanation	PR	Debit	Credit
a.					
b.					
c.					

Name: _____

Exercise 3-7 (concl'd.)

Date	Account Titles and Explanation	PR	Debit	Credit
d.				

Part 2

GENERAL JOURNAL

Page_____

Date	Account Titles and Explanation	PR	Debit	Credit
a.				
b.				
c.				
d.				
e.				
f.				

Name: _____

Exercise 3-8

GENERAL JOURNAL

Page____

Date	Account Titles and Explanation	PR	Debit	Credit
a.				
b.				
c.				
d.				
e.				

Fundamental Accounting Principles, 16ce, Working Papers

Name: _____

Exercise 3-8 (concl'd.)

Date	Account Titles and Explanation	PR	Debit	Credit
f.				
g.				

Exercise 3-9

GENERAL JOURNAL   Page_____

Date	Account Titles and Explanation	PR	Debit	Credit
1.				
2.				
a.				
b.				
c.				
d.				

Exercise 3-10

GENERAL JOURNAL

Page_____

Date	Account Titles and Explanation	PR	Debit	Credit
a.				
b.				
c.				
d.				
e.				
f.				

Name: _____

Exercise 3-11

GENERAL JOURNAL

Page_____

	Date	Account Titles and Explanation	PR	Debit	Credit
a.					
b.					
c.					

Exercise 3-12

GENERAL JOURNAL

Page_____

	Date	Account Titles and Explanation	PR	Debit	Credit
a.					
b.					
c.					
d.					
e.					

Name: _____

Exercise 3-13

a. _____
_____
_____
_____

b. _____
_____
_____

c. _____
_____
_____

d. _____
_____
_____

Exercise 3-14

Adjusting Entry:

GENERAL JOURNAL
Page____

Date	Account Titles and Explanation	PR	Debit	Credit

Payday Entry:

GENERAL JOURNAL
Page____

Date	Account Titles and Explanation	PR	Debit	Credit

Name: _____

Exercise 3-15

(a)
Adjusting Entry:

GENERAL JOURNAL   Page____

Date	Account Titles and Explanation	PR	Debit	Credit

Journal Entry (Next Period):

GENERAL JOURNAL   Page____

Date	Account Titles and Explanation	PR	Debit	Credit

(b)
Adjusting Entry:

GENERAL JOURNAL   Page____

Date	Account Titles and Explanation	PR	Debit	Credit

Journal Entry (Next Period):

GENERAL JOURNAL   Page____

Date	Account Titles and Explanation	PR	Debit	Credit

Name: _____

Exercise 3-15 (concl'd.)

(c)
Adjusting Entry:

GENERAL JOURNAL   Page____

Date	Account Titles and Explanation	PR	Debit	Credit

Journal Entry (Next Period):

GENERAL JOURNAL   Page____

Date	Account Titles and Explanation	PR	Debit	Credit

Exercise 3-16

GENERAL JOURNAL   Page____

Date	Account Titles and Explanation	PR	Debit	Credit

Fundamental Accounting Principles, 16ce, Working Papers

Exercise 3-16 (concl'd.)

GENERAL JOURNAL

Page_____

Date		Account Titles and Explanation	PR	Debit	Credit

Analysis component:

_____

_____

_____

_____

_____

_____

Name: _____

Exercise 3-17

ACCOUNT	UNADJUSTED TRIAL BALANCE		ADJUSTMENT		ADJUSTED TRIAL BALANCE	
	Debit	Credit	Debit	Credit	Debit	Credit
Cash	$ 14,000					
Accounts receivable	32,000					
Prepaid insurance	16,800					
Equipment	102,000					
Accum. deprec., equipment		$ 23,000				
Accounts payable		19,000				
Abraham Nuna, capital		213,000				
Abraham Nuna, withdrawals	102,000					
Revenues		214,000				
Deprec. exp., equipment	-0-					
Salaries expense	187,700					
Insurance expense	14,500					
Totals	$469,000	$469,000				

Exercise 3-18

Income Statement

Statement of Changes in Equity

Name: _____

Exercise 3-18 (concl'd.)

Balance Sheet		

Analysis component:

_____
_____
_____
_____
_____

*Exercise 3-19

GENERAL JOURNAL

Page_____

Date		Account Titles and Explanation	PR	Debit	Credit
a.					
b.					

Name: _____

*Exercise 3-19 (concl'd.)

GENERAL JOURNAL

Page_____

Date	Account Titles and Explanation	PR	Debit	Credit
c.				
d.				

Analysis component:

_____

_____

_____

_____

_____

_____

Name: _____

*Exercise 3-20

GENERAL JOURNAL

Page_____

Date	Account Titles and Explanation	PR	Debit	Credit
a.				
b.				
c.				
d.				
e.				
f.				

Name: _____

*Exercise 3-21

a. Initial credit recorded in Unearned Revenue account:

		GENERAL JOURNAL			Page____
Date		Account Titles and Explanation	PR	Debit	Credit

Name: _____

*Exercise 3-21 (concl'd.)

b. Initial credit recorded in Revenue account:

GENERAL JOURNAL

Page____

Date	Account Titles and Explanation	PR	Debit	Credit

c.

_____
_____
_____
_____
_____
_____
_____
_____
_____

Name: _____

Problem 3-1A

GENERAL JOURNAL   Page____

Date	Account Titles and Explanation	PR	Debit	Credit
a.				
b.				
c.				
d.				

Analysis component:

_____

_____

_____

_____

Problem 3-2A

GENERAL JOURNAL   Page____

Date	Account Titles and Explanation	PR	Debit	Credit
a.				
b.				
c.				

Fundamental Accounting Principles, 16ce, Working Papers

Name: _____

Problem 3-2A (concl'd.)

Analysis component:

_____
_____
_____
_____
_____
_____
_____
_____
_____

Problem 3-3A

GENERAL JOURNAL

Page____

Date		Account Titles and Explanation	PR	Debit	Credit
a.					
b.					
c.					
d.					

Analysis component:

_____
_____
_____
_____
_____
_____
_____
_____
_____

Name: _____

Problem 3-4A

Adjusting Entries: **GENERAL JOURNAL**   Page_____

Date	Account Titles and Explanation	PR	Debit	Credit
a.				
b.				
c.				
d.				
e.				

Name: _____

Problem 3-4A (concl'd.)

Subsequent Entries: **GENERAL JOURNAL**   Page_____

Date		Account Titles and Explanation	PR	Debit	Credit
a.					
b.					
c.					
d.					
e.					

Name: _____

Problem 3-5A

Adjusting Entries: **GENERAL JOURNAL**   Page_____

Date	Account Titles and Explanation	PR	Debit	Credit
a.				
b.				
c.				
d.				

Subsequent Entries: **GENERAL JOURNAL**   Page_____

Date	Account Titles and Explanation	PR	Debit	Credit
a.				
b.				
c.				
d.				

Name: _____

Problem 3-6A

Part 1:

GENERAL JOURNAL

Page_____

Date		Account Titles and Explanation	PR	Debit	Credit
a.					
b.					
c.					
d.					
e.					
f.					
g.					
h.					

Part 2: *See next page for Part 2 working paper.*

Part 3: _____
_____
_____

Part 4: _____
_____
_____
_____

Name: _____

Problem 3-6A (concl'd.)

Part 2

ACCOUNT	UNADJUSTED TRIAL BALANCE		ADJUSTMENTS		ADJUSTED TRIAL BALANCE	
	Debit	Credit	Debit	Credit	Debit	Credit
Cash	$ 18,000					
Accounts receivable	-0-					
Teaching supplies	6,500					
Prepaid insurance	1,400					
Prepaid rent	7,200					
Professional library	60,000					
Accum. deprec., professional library		18,000				
Equipment	96,000					
Accum. deprec., equipment		32,000				
Accounts payable		2,500				
Salaries payable		-0-				
Unearned extension revenue		6,300				
Karoo Ashevak, capital		229,000				
Karoo Ashevak, withdrwls	92,000					
Tuition revenue		196,000				
Extension revenue		72,500				
Deprec. exp., equipment	-0-					
Deprec. exp., prof library	-0-					
Salaries expense	206,000					
Insurance expense	-0-					
Rent expense	44,000					
Teaching supplies expense	-0-					
Advertising expense	14,000					
Utilities expense	11,200					
Totals	$556,300	$556,300				

Problem 3-7A

GENERAL JOURNAL   Page____

Date		Account Titles and Explanation	PR	Debit	Credit
a.					
b.					

Fundamental Accounting Principles, 16ce, Working Papers

Name: _____

Problem 3-7A (concl'd.)

GENERAL JOURNAL   Page____

Date	Account Titles and Explanation	PR	Debit	Credit
c.				
d.				
e.				
f.				
g.				
h.				
i.				
j.				

Name: _____

Problem 3-8A

Part 1   **GENERAL JOURNAL**   Page____

Date	Account Titles and Explanation	PR	Debit	Credit
a.				
b.				
c.				
d.				
e.				
f.				

Problem 3-8A (concl'd.)

Part 2   **GENERAL JOURNAL**   Page____

Date	Account Titles and Explanation	PR	Debit	Credit

Problem 3-9A

GENERAL JOURNAL   Page____

Date	Account Titles and Explanation	PR	Debit	Credit
a.				
b.				
c.				
d.				

Name: _____

Problem 3-9A (concl'd.)

GENERAL JOURNAL   Page____

Date	Account Titles and Explanation	PR	Debit	Credit
e.				
f.				
g.				
h.				
i.				

Name: _____

Problem 3-10A

Parts 1 and 2 (in balance column account format)

Note: The T-account template is provided at the end of this question.

GENERAL LEDGER

Cash   ACCOUNT NO. 101

DATE	EXPLANATION	PR	DEBIT	CREDIT	BALANCE
2020					
Oct. 31	Balance				26,000

Accounts Receivable   ACCOUNT NO. 106

DATE	EXPLANATION	PR	DEBIT	CREDIT	BALANCE
2020					
Oct. 31	Balance				61,000

Interest Receivable   ACCOUNT NO. 109

DATE	EXPLANATION	PR	DEBIT	CREDIT	BALANCE
2020					

Notes Receivable   ACCOUNT NO. 111

DATE	EXPLANATION	PR	DEBIT	CREDIT	BALANCE
2020					
Oct. 31	Balance				50,000

Supplies   ACCOUNT NO. 126

DATE	EXPLANATION	PR	DEBIT	CREDIT	BALANCE
2020					
Oct. 31	Balance				5,300

Prepaid Insurance   ACCOUNT NO. 128

DATE	EXPLANATION	PR	DEBIT	CREDIT	BALANCE
2020					
Oct. 31	Balance				3,400

Problem 3-10A (cont'd.)

Prepaid Rent   ACCOUNT NO. 131

DATE	EXPLANATION	PR	DEBIT	CREDIT	BALANCE
2020					
Oct. 31	Balance				27,000

Office Furniture   ACCOUNT NO. 161

DATE	EXPLANATION	PR	DEBIT	CREDIT	BALANCE
2020					
Oct. 31	Balance				84,000

Accumulated Depreciation, Office Furniture   ACCOUNT NO. 162

DATE	EXPLANATION	PR	DEBIT	CREDIT	BALANCE
2020					
Oct. 31	Balance				28,000

Accounts Payable   ACCOUNT NO. 201

DATE	EXPLANATION	PR	DEBIT	CREDIT	BALANCE
2020					
Oct. 31	Balance				18,000

Wages Payable   ACCOUNT NO. 210

DATE	EXPLANATION	PR	DEBIT	CREDIT	BALANCE
2020					

Unearned Consulting Revenue   ACCOUNT NO. 233

DATE	EXPLANATION	PR	DEBIT	CREDIT	BALANCE
2020					
Oct. 31	Balance				26,000

Jeff Moore, Capital   ACCOUNT NO. 301

DATE	EXPLANATION	PR	DEBIT	CREDIT	BALANCE
2020					
Oct. 31	Balance				223,000

Problem 3-10A (cont'd.)

Jeff Moore, Withdrawals   ACCOUNT NO. 302

DATE	EXPLANATION	PR	DEBIT	CREDIT	BALANCE
2020					
Oct. 31	Balance				28,000

Consulting Revenue   ACCOUNT NO. 401

DATE	EXPLANATION	PR	DEBIT	CREDIT	BALANCE
2020					
Oct. 31	Balance				232,020

Interest Income   ACCOUNT NO. 409

DATE	EXPLANATION	PR	DEBIT	CREDIT	BALANCE
2020					
Oct. 31	Balance				480

Depreciation Expense, Office Furniture   ACCOUNT NO. 601

DATE	EXPLANATION	PR	DEBIT	CREDIT	BALANCE
2020					

Wages Expense   ACCOUNT NO. 622

DATE	EXPLANATION	PR	DEBIT	CREDIT	BALANCE
2020					
Oct. 31	Balance				192,000

Insurance Expense   ACCOUNT NO. 637

DATE	EXPLANATION	PR	DEBIT	CREDIT	BALANCE
2020					

Problem 3-10A (cont'd.)

	Rent Expense			ACCOUNT NO. 640	
DATE	EXPLANATION	PR	DEBIT	CREDIT	BALANCE
2020					
Oct. 31	Balance				44,000

	Supplies Expense			ACCOUNT NO. 650	
DATE	EXPLANATION	PR	DEBIT	CREDIT	BALANCE
2020					
Oct. 31	Balance				6,800

Name: _____

Problem 3-10A (cont'd.) Part 3

Adjusted Trial Balance

Part 4

Income Statement

Problem 3-10A (cont'd.)

Statement of Changes in Equity

Balance Sheet

Analysis component:

Problem 3-10A (cont'd.)

Part 1 and 2 (in T-account format)

Cash	101
Unadj Bal	
Oct 31 26,000	

Accounts Receivable	106
Unadj Bal	
Oct 31 61,000	

Interest Receivable	109

Notes Receivable	111
Unadj Bal	
Oct 31 50,000	

Supplies	126
Unadj Bal	
Oct 31 5,300	

Prepaid Insurance	128
Unadj Bal	
Oct 31 3,400	

Prepaid Rent	131
Unadj Bal	
Oct 31 27,000	

Office Furniture	161
Unadj Bal	
Oct 31 84,000	

Accum. Deprec., Office Furniture	162
	Unadj Bal
	Oct 31 28,000

Accounts Payable	201
	Unadj Bal
	Oct 31 18,000

Wages Payable	210

Unearned Consulting Revenue	233
	Unadj Bal
	Oct 31 26,000

Problem 3-10A (concl'd.)

Jeff Moore, Capital	301
	Unadj Bal Oct 31 223,000

Jeff Moore, Withdrawals	302
Unadj Bal Oct 31 28,000	

Consulting Revenue	401
	Unadj Bal Oct 31 232,020

Interest Income	409
	Unadj Bal Oct 31 480

Deprec. Expense, Office Furniture	601

Wages Expense	622
Unadj Bal Oct 31 192,000	

Insurance Expense	637

Rent Expense	640
Unadj Bal Oct 31 44,000	

Supplies Expense	650
Unadj Bal Oct 31 6,800	

Name: _____

Problem 3-11A

GENERAL JOURNAL

Page_____

Date	Account Titles and Explanation	PR	Debit	Credit
a.				
b.				
c.				
d.				
e.				
f.				
g.				

Name: _____

Problem 3-12A   Part 1

ACCOUNT	UNADJUSTED TRIAL BALANCE Debit	UNADJUSTED TRIAL BALANCE Credit	ADJUSTMENTS Debit	ADJUSTMENTS Credit	ADJUSTED TRIAL BALANCE Debit	ADJUSTED TRIAL BALANCE Credit
Cash	$ 6,000					
Accounts receivable	11,200					
Repair supplies	2,200					
Prepaid rent	14,000					
Office furniture	26,000					
Accounts payable		$ 8,000				
Notes payable		21,600				
Eli Arrow, capital		67,758				
Eli Arrow, withdrawals	5,000					
Hospitality revenues		128,000				
Salaries expense	144,000					
Wages expense	16,958					
Totals	$225,358	$225,358				

Part 2

Income Statement

Name: _____

Problem 3-12A (concl'd.)

Statement of Changes in Equity

Balance Sheet

Analysis component:

_____

_____

_____

_____

_____

_____

_____

_____

Name: _____

Problem 3-13A

Part 1

Income Statement

Part 2

Statement of Changes in Equity

Fundamental Accounting Principles, 16ce, Working Papers

Name: _____

Problem 3-13A (concl'd.)

Part 3

Balance Sheet		

Analysis component:

_____
_____
_____
_____
_____
_____
_____
_____

GENERAL JOURNAL

Page____

Date		Account Titles and Explanation	PR	Debit	Credit

Name: _____

Problem 3-14A (cont'd.)

Parts 2, 3 and 5

Cash	101		Prepaid Rent	131

Office Furniture	161		Accum. Deprec., Office Furn.	162

Accounts Payable	201		Unearned Revenue	233

Mark Diamond, Capital	301		Mark Diamond, Withdrawals	302

Revenue	401		Deprec. Exp., Office Furniture	602

Wages Expense	623		Rent Expense	640

Telephone Expense	688		Hotel Expenses	696

Name: _____

Problem 3-14A (cont'd.)

Part 4

Trial Balance	Debit	Credit

Part 5 – Adjusting entries

GENERAL JOURNAL Page____

Date	Account Titles and Explanation	PR	Debit	Credit

Name: _____

Problem 3-14A (cont'd.)

Part 6

Trial Balance

	Debit	Credit

Part 7

Income Statement

Name: _____

Problem 3-14A (concl'd.)

Part 7 (concl'd.)

Statement of Changes in Equity

Balance Sheet

Analysis component:

Name: _____

*Problem 3-15A

		GENERAL JOURNAL			Page____
Date		**Account Titles and Explanation**	**PR**	**Debit**	**Credit**
a.					
b.					
c.					
d.					
e.					

Analysis component:

_____
_____
_____
_____
_____
_____
_____

Name: _____

*Problem 3-16A

ACCOUNT	UNADJUSTED TRIAL BALANCE		ADJUSTMENTS		ADJUSTED TRIAL BALANCE	
	Debit	Credit	Debit	Credit	Debit	Credit
Cash	$ 32,000					
Accounts receivable	63,000					
Prepaid rent	-0-					
Prepaid insurance	-0-					
Accounts payable		$ 16,000				
Unearned consulting revenue		-0-				
Bruce Willis, capital		38,400				
Consulting revenue		82,000				
Rent expense	38,990					
Insurance expense	2,410					
Totals	$136,400	$136,400				

*Problem 3-17A

Part 1 - Entries that initially recognize assets and liabilities:

GENERAL JOURNAL

Page____

Date	Account Titles and Explanation	PR	Debit	Credit

Fundamental Accounting Principles, 16ce, Working Papers

Name: _____

*Problem 3-17A (cont'd.)

GENERAL JOURNAL

Page____

Date	Account Titles and Explanation	PR	Debit	Credit

Part 2 – Entries that initially recognize expenses and revenues:

GENERAL JOURNAL

Page____

Date	Account Titles and Explanation	PR	Debit	Credit

Name: _____

*Problem 3-17A (concl'd.)

Part 2 (concluded)

GENERAL JOURNAL

Page_____

Date	Account Titles and Explanation	PR	Debit	Credit

Analysis component:

_____
_____
_____
_____
_____
_____
_____
_____
_____
_____
_____
_____
_____
_____
_____
_____

Name: _____

Problem 3-1B

GENERAL JOURNAL

Page____

Date		Account Titles and Explanation	PR	Debit	Credit
a.					
b.					
c.					
d.					

Analysis component:

_____

_____

_____

_____

Problem 3-2B

GENERAL JOURNAL

Page____

Date		Account Titles and Explanation	PR	Debit	Credit
a.					
b.					
c.					

Name: _____

Problem 3-2B (concl'd.)

Analysis component:

_____
_____
_____
_____
_____
_____
_____
_____
_____

Problem 3-3B

GENERAL JOURNAL

Page____

Date	Account Titles and Explanation	PR	Debit	Credit
a.				
b.				
c.				
d.				

Analysis component:

_____
_____
_____
_____
_____
_____
_____
_____

Name: _____

Problem 3-4B

Adjusting Entries: **GENERAL JOURNAL**   Page____

Date		Account Titles and Explanation	PR	Debit	Credit
a.					
b.					
c.					
d.					
e.					

Problem 3-4B (concl'd.)

Subsequent Entries: GENERAL JOURNAL   Page_____

Date	Account Titles and Explanation	PR	Debit	Credit
a.				
b.				
c.				
d.				
e.				

Name: _____

Problem 3-5B

Adjusting Entries: **GENERAL JOURNAL**   Page_____

Date		Account Titles and Explanation	PR	Debit	Credit
a.					
b.					
c.					
d.					

Subsequent Entries: **GENERAL JOURNAL**   Page_____

Date		Account Titles and Explanation	PR	Debit	Credit
a.					
b.					
c.					
d.					

Name: _____

Problem 3-6B

Part 1

GENERAL JOURNAL

Page_____

Date		Account Titles and Explanation	PR	Debit	Credit
a.					
b.					
c.					
d.					
e.					
f.					
g.					
h.					

Part 2: *See next page for Part 2 working paper.*

Part 3: _____

_____

_____

Part 4: _____

_____

_____

_____

Name: _____

Problem 3-6B (concl'd.)

Part 2

ACCOUNT	UNADJUSTED TRIAL BALANCE Debit	UNADJUSTED TRIAL BALANCE Credit	ADJUSTMENTS Debit	ADJUSTMENTS Credit	ADJUSTED TRIAL BALANCE Debit	ADJUSTED TRIAL BALANCE Credit
Cash	$ 25,000					
Accounts receivable	-0-					
Teaching supplies	107,200					
Prepaid insurance	36,000					
Prepaid rent	11,600					
Professional library	20,000					
Accum. deprec., professional library		3,000				
Equipment	141,400					
Accum. deprec., equipment		32,000				
Accounts payable		24,400				
Salaries payable		-0-				
Unearned extension revenue		55,200				
Jay Fawcett, capital		62,000				
Jay Fawcett, withdrawals	40,000					
Tuition revenue		285,000				
Extension revenue		124,000				
Deprec. exp., equipment	-0-					
Deprec. exp., profl library	-0-					
Salaries expense	143,600					
Insurance expense	-0-					
Rent expense	-0-					
Teaching supplies expense	-0-					
Advertising expense	36,000					
Utilities expense	24,800					
Totals	$585,600	$585,600				

Problem 3-7B

Subsequent Entries:

GENERAL JOURNAL

Page_____

Date		Account Titles and Explanation	PR	Debit	Credit
a.					
b.					

Name: _____

Problem 3-7B (concl'd.)

GENERAL JOURNAL

Page_____

Date	Account Titles and Explanation	PR	Debit	Credit
c.				
d.				
e.				
f.				
g.				
h.				
i.				
j.				

Fundamental Accounting Principles, 16ce, Working Papers

Chapter 3

Name: _____

Problem 3-8B

Part 1 **GENERAL JOURNAL** Page____

Date		Account Titles and Explanation	PR	Debit	Credit
a.					
b.					
c.					
d.					
e.					
f.					

Name: _____

Problem 3-8B (concl'd.)

Part 2   GENERAL JOURNAL   Page_____

Date	Account Titles and Explanation	PR	Debit	Credit

Problem 3-9B

GENERAL JOURNAL   Page_____

Date	Account Titles and Explanation	PR	Debit	Credit
a.				
b.				
c.				
d.				

Name: _____

Problem 3-9B (concl'd.)

GENERAL JOURNAL

Page_____

Date	Account Titles and Explanation	PR	Debit	Credit
e.				
f.				
g.				
h.				
i.				

Analysis component:

_____

_____

_____

_____

_____

_____

_____

_____

Name: _____

Problem 3-10B

Parts 1 and 2

Cash   ACCOUNT NO. 101

DATE	EXPLANATION	PR	DEBIT	CREDIT	BALANCE
2020					
Dec. 31	Balance				15,600

Accounts Receivable   ACCOUNT NO. 106

DATE	EXPLANATION	PR	DEBIT	CREDIT	BALANCE
2020					
Dec. 31	Balance				29,200

Supplies   ACCOUNT NO. 126

DATE	EXPLANATION	PR	DEBIT	CREDIT	BALANCE
2020					
Dec. 31	Balance				1,640

Prepaid Advertising   ACCOUNT NO. 128

DATE	EXPLANATION	PR	DEBIT	CREDIT	BALANCE
2020					
Dec. 31	Balance				1,280

Prepaid Rent   ACCOUNT NO. 131

DATE	EXPLANATION	PR	DEBIT	CREDIT	BALANCE
2020					
Dec. 31	Balance				17,880

Surveying Equipment   ACCOUNT NO. 167

DATE	EXPLANATION	PR	DEBIT	CREDIT	BALANCE
2020					
Dec. 31	Balance				58,000

Accum. Deprec. – Surveying Equipment   ACCOUNT NO. 168

DATE	EXPLANATION	PR	DEBIT	CREDIT	BALANCE
2020					
Dec. 31	Balance				7,348

Fundamental Accounting Principles, 16ce, Working Papers

Name: _____

Problem 3-10B (cont'd.)

Accounts Payable — ACCOUNT NO. 201

DATE	EXPLANATION	PR	DEBIT	CREDIT	BALANCE
2020					
Dec. 31	Balance				13,800

Interest Payable — ACCOUNT NO. 203

DATE	EXPLANATION	PR	DEBIT	CREDIT	BALANCE
2020					

Wages Payable — ACCOUNT NO. 210

DATE	EXPLANATION	PR	DEBIT	CREDIT	BALANCE
2020					

Unearned Surveying Revenue — ACCOUNT NO. 233

DATE	EXPLANATION	PR	DEBIT	CREDIT	BALANCE
2020					
Dec. 31	Balance				14,800

Notes Payable — ACCOUNT NO. 251

DATE	EXPLANATION	PR	DEBIT	CREDIT	BALANCE
2020					
Dec. 31	Balance				36,000

Ben Hallmark, Capital — ACCOUNT NO. 301

DATE	EXPLANATION	PR	DEBIT	CREDIT	BALANCE
2020					
Dec. 31	Balance				28,652

Ben Hallmark, Withdrawals — ACCOUNT NO. 302

DATE	EXPLANATION	PR	DEBIT	CREDIT	BALANCE
2020					
Dec. 31	Balance				24,300

Problem 3-10B (cont'd.)

Surveying Revenue   ACCOUNT NO. 401

DATE	EXPLANATION	PR	DEBIT	CREDIT	BALANCE
2020					
Dec. 31	Balance				170,948

Depreciation Expense, Surveying Equipment   ACCOUNT NO. 601

DATE	EXPLANATION	PR	DEBIT	CREDIT	BALANCE
2020					

Salaries Expense   ACCOUNT NO. 622

DATE	EXPLANATION	PR	DEBIT	CREDIT	BALANCE
2020					
Dec. 31	Balance				56,000

Wages Expense   ACCOUNT NO. 623

DATE	EXPLANATION	PR	DEBIT	CREDIT	BALANCE
2020					
Dec. 31	Balance				39,726

Interest Expense   ACCOUNT NO. 633

DATE	EXPLANATION	PR	DEBIT	CREDIT	BALANCE
2020					

Insurance Expense   ACCOUNT NO. 637

DATE	EXPLANATION	PR	DEBIT	CREDIT	BALANCE
2020					
Dec. 31	Balance				6,000

Rent Expense   ACCOUNT NO. 640

DATE	EXPLANATION	PR	DEBIT	CREDIT	BALANCE
2020					

Supplies Expense — ACCOUNT NO. 650

DATE	EXPLANATION	PR	DEBIT	CREDIT	BALANCE
2020					
Dec. 31	Balance				2,958

Advertising Expense — ACCOUNT NO. 655

DATE	EXPLANATION	PR	DEBIT	CREDIT	BALANCE
2020					

Gas and Oil Expense — ACCOUNT NO. 671

DATE	EXPLANATION	PR	DEBIT	CREDIT	BALANCE
2020					
Dec. 31	Balance				6,564

Repairs Expense — ACCOUNT NO. 684

DATE	EXPLANATION	PR	DEBIT	CREDIT	BALANCE
2020					
Dec. 31	Balance				12,400

Utilities Expense — ACCOUNT NO. 690

DATE	EXPLANATION	PR	DEBIT	CREDIT	BALANCE
2020					

Problem 3-10B (cont'd.) Part 3

Adjusted Trial Balance

Fundamental Accounting Principles, 16ce, Working Papers

Name: _____

Problem 3-10B (cont'd.) Part 4

Income Statement

Statement of Changes in Equity

Problem 3-10B (concl'd.)

	Balance Sheet		

Analysis component:

_____
_____
_____
_____
_____
_____
_____
_____
_____
_____
_____

Name: _____

Problem 3-11B

GENERAL JOURNAL

Page_____

Date	Account Titles and Explanation	PR	Debit	Credit
a.				
b.				
c.				
d.				
e.				
f.				
g.				

Name: _____

Problem 3-12B Part 1

ACCOUNT	UNADJUSTED TRIAL BALANCE		ADJUSTMENTS		ADJUSTED TRIAL BALANCE	
	Debit	Credit	Debit	Credit	Debit	Credit
Cash	$ 112,000					
Accounts receivable	28,000					
Repair supplies	2,800					
Prepaid arena rental	182,000					
Skate equipment	428,000					
Accum. deprec., skate eq.		$ 164,000				
Accounts payable		5,400				
Unearned training revenue		19,600				
Notes payable		160,000				
Ben Gibson, capital		451,400				
Ben Gibson, withdrawals	72,000					
Training revenue		550,000				
Salaries expense	350,000					
Arena rental expense	168,000					
Other expenses	7,600					
Totals	$1,350,400	$1,350,400				

Part 2

Income Statement

Name: _____

Problem 3-12B (concl'd.)

Statement of Changes in Equity

Balance Sheet

Analysis component:

_____
_____
_____
_____
_____
_____
_____

Name: _____

Problem 3-13B

Part 1

Income Statement		

Part 2

Statement of Changes in Equity		

Name: _____

Problem 3-13B (concl'd.)

Part 3

Balance Sheet

Name: _____

Problem 3-14B   Part 1

GENERAL JOURNAL

Page_____

Date	Account Titles and Explanation	PR	Debit	Credit

Problem 3-14B (cont'd.)

Parts 2, 3, and 5

Cash	101		Repair Supplies	131
Bal. 6,400			Bal. 3,000	

Tools	161		Accum. Deprec., Tools	162
Bal. 16,800			560	Bal.

			Unearned Revenue	233
			700	Bal.

Accounts Payable	201
3,200	Bal.

Melanie Thornhill, Capital	301		Melanie Thornhill, Withdrawals	302
	Bal.		Bal. -0-	

Revenue	401		Deprec. Exp., Tools	602
25,800	Bal.		Bal. 560	

Wages Expense	623		Rent Expense	640
Bal. 1,960			Bal. 8,000	

Repair Supplies Expense	696
Bal. 2,700	

Name: _____

Problem 3-14B (cont'd.)

Part 4

Trial Balance

	Debit	Credit

Part 5 – Adjusting entries

GENERAL JOURNAL

Page_____

Date		Account Titles and Explanation	PR	Debit	Credit

Problem 3-14B (cont'd.)

Part 6

Trial Balance

	Debit	Credit

Part 7

Income Statement

Name: _____

Problem 3-14B (concl'd.)

Part 6 (concl'd.)

Statement of Changes in Equity

Balance Sheet

Analysis component:

_____

_____

_____

_____

_____

_____

_____

Name: _____

*Problem 3-15B

GENERAL JOURNAL

Page____

Date	Account Titles and Explanation	PR	Debit	Credit
a.				
b.				
c.				
d.				
e.				

Analysis component:

_____
_____
_____
_____
_____
_____
_____

*Problem 3-16B

ACCOUNT	UNADJUSTED TRIAL BALANCE		ADJUSTMENTS		ADJUSTED TRIAL BALAN	
	Debit	Credit	Debit	Credit	Debit	Cre
Cash	$ 3,500					
Accounts receivable	7,200					
Prepaid advertising	-0-					
Cleaning supplies	-0-					
Equipment	29,000					
Accum. deprec., equipment		$ 3,200				
Unearned window washing revenue		-0-				
Unearned office cleaning revenue		-0-				
William Nahanee, capital		9,150				
Window washing revenue		23,800				
Office cleaning revenue		71,500				
Advertising expense	2,900					
Salaries expense	56,900					
Depreciation expense, equip.	-0-					
Cleaning supplies expense	8,150					
Totals	$107,650	$107,650				

*Problem 3-17B

Part 1 - Entries that initially recognize assets and liabilities:

GENERAL JOURNAL   Page_____

Date	Account Titles and Explanation	PR	Debit	Credit

Name: _____

*Problem 3-17B (cont'd.)

GENERAL JOURNAL

Page____

Date		Account Titles and Explanation	PR	Debit	Credit

Part 2 – Entries that initially recognize expenses and revenues:

GENERAL JOURNAL

Page____

Date		Account Titles and Explanation	PR	Debit	Credit

Name: _____

*Problem 3-17B (concl'd.)

Part 2 (concl'd)

GENERAL JOURNAL   Page____

Date		Account Titles and Explanation	PR	Debit	Credit

Analysis component:

_____
_____
_____
_____
_____
_____
_____
_____
_____
_____
_____
_____
_____
_____
_____
_____

Name: _____

Cumulative Problem

Part 1   **Echo Systems**
             Journal Entries

GENERAL JOURNAL

Page____

Date	Account Titles and Explanation	PR	Debit	Credit

Name: _____

Cumulative Problem

Part 2   Echo Systems
              Adjusting Entries

GENERAL JOURNAL

Page____

Date	Account Titles and Explanation	PR	Debit	Credit

Cumulative Problem

Part 2   **Echo Systems (Cont'd.)**

GENERAL LEDGER

Cash   ACCOUNT NO. 101

DATE	EXPLANATION	PR	DEBIT	CREDIT	BALANCE
2020 Nov. 30	Balance				70,340

Accounts Receivable   ACCOUNT NO. 106

DATE	EXPLANATION	PR	DEBIT	CREDIT	BALANCE
2020 Nov. 30	Balance				18,900

Computer Supplies   ACCOUNT NO. 126

DATE	EXPLANATION	PR	DEBIT	CREDIT	BALANCE
2020 Nov. 30	Balance				4,560

Prepaid Insurance   ACCOUNT NO. 128

DATE	EXPLANATION	PR	DEBIT	CREDIT	BALANCE
2020 Nov. 30	Balance				4,320

Prepaid Rent   ACCOUNT NO. 131

DATE	EXPLANATION	PR	DEBIT	CREDIT	BALANCE
2020 Nov. 30	Balance				9,000

Cumulative Problem

Part 2   **Echo Systems (Cont'd.)**

Office Equipment   ACCOUNT NO. 163

DATE	EXPLANATION	PR	DEBIT	CREDIT	BALANCE
2020 Nov. 30	Balance				18,000

Accumulated Depreciation, Office Equipment   ACCOUNT NO. 164

DATE	EXPLANATION	PR	DEBIT	CREDIT	BALANCE
2020 Nov. 30	Balance				-0-

Computer Equipment   ACCOUNT NO. 167

DATE	EXPLANATION	PR	DEBIT	CREDIT	BALANCE
2020 Nov. 30	Balance				36,000

Accumulated Depreciation, Computer Equipment   ACCOUNT NO. 168

DATE	EXPLANATION	PR	DEBIT	CREDIT	BALANCE
2020 Nov. 30	Balance				-0-

Accounts Payable   ACCOUNT NO. 201

DATE	EXPLANATION	PR	DEBIT	CREDIT	BALANCE
2020 Nov. 30	Balance				-0-

Wages Payable   ACCOUNT NO. 210

DATE	EXPLANATION	PR	DEBIT	CREDIT	BALANCE
2020 Nov. 30	Balance				-0-

Unearned Computer Services Revenue   ACCOUNT NO. 236

DATE	EXPLANATION	PR	DEBIT	CREDIT	BALANCE
2020 Nov. 30	Balance				-0-

Mary Graham, Capital   ACCOUNT NO. 301

DATE	EXPLANATION	PR	DEBIT	CREDIT	BALANCE
2020 Nov. 30	Balance				144,000

Chapter 3

Name: _____

Cumulative Problem

Part 2   Echo Systems (Cont'd.)

Mary Graham, Withdrawals   ACCOUNT NO. 302

DATE	EXPLANATION	PR	DEBIT	CREDIT	BALANCE
2020 Nov. 30	Balance				10,800

Computer Services Revenue   ACCOUNT NO. 403

DATE	EXPLANATION	PR	DEBIT	CREDIT	BALANCE
2020 Nov. 30	Balance				40,950

Depreciation Expense, Office Equipment   ACCOUNT NO. 612

DATE	EXPLANATION	PR	DEBIT	CREDIT	BALANCE
2020 Nov. 30	Balance				-0-

Depreciation Expense, Computer Equipment   ACCOUNT NO. 613

DATE	EXPLANATION	PR	DEBIT	CREDIT	BALANCE
2020 Nov. 30	Balance				-0-

Wages Expense   ACCOUNT NO. 623

DATE	EXPLANATION	PR	DEBIT	CREDIT	BALANCE
2020 Nov. 30	Balance				4,200

Insurance Expense   ACCOUNT NO. 637

DATE	EXPLANATION	PR	DEBIT	CREDIT	BALANCE
2020 Nov. 30	Balance				-0-

Rent Expense   ACCOUNT NO. 640

DATE	EXPLANATION	PR	DEBIT	CREDIT	BALANCE
2020 Nov. 30	Balance				-0-

Cumulative Problem

Part 2   **Echo Systems (Cont'd.)**

Computer Supplies Expense   ACCOUNT NO. 652

DATE	EXPLANATION	PR	DEBIT	CREDIT	BALANCE
2020 Nov. 30	Balance				-0-

Advertising Expense   ACCOUNT NO. 655

DATE	EXPLANATION	PR	DEBIT	CREDIT	BALANCE
2020 Nov. 30	Balance				3,720

Mileage Expense   ACCOUNT NO. 676

DATE	EXPLANATION	PR	DEBIT	CREDIT	BALANCE
2020 Nov. 30	Balance				2,200

Repairs Expense, Computer   ACCOUNT NO. 684

DATE	EXPLANATION	PR	DEBIT	CREDIT	BALANCE
2020 Nov. 30	Balance				1,410

Charitable Donations Expense   ACCOUNT NO. 699

DATE	EXPLANATION	PR	DEBIT	CREDIT	BALANCE
2020 Nov. 30	Balance				1,500

Cumulative Problem

Part 3　　　　　Echo Systems (Cont'd.)

ECHO SYSTEMS
Adjusted Trial Balance
December 31, 2020

	Debit	Credit

Cumulative Problem

Part 4   Echo Systems (Cont'd.)

ECHO SYSTEMS
Income Statement
For Three Months Ended December 31, 2020

ECHO SYSTEMS
Statement of Changes in Equity
For Three Months Ended December 31, 2020

Name: _____

Cumulative Problem

Part 5   **Echo Systems (Concl'd.)**

ECHO SYSTEMS		
Balance Sheet		
December 31, 2020		

Chapter 4

Quick Study 4-1

1. _BS_ Equipment
2. _BS_ Owner, withdrawals
3. _IS_ Insurance expense

4. _BS_ Prepaid insurance
5. _BS_ Accounts receivable
6. _IS_ Depreciation expense, equipment

Quick Study 4-2

-see next page for QS 4-2 working paper

Quick Study 4-3

50,000 + 184,000 - 125,000 - 32,000 = $77,000

Quick Study 4-4

Quick Study 4-2

Account Title	Unadjusted Trial Balance Debit	Unadjusted Trial Balance Credit	Adjustments Debit	Adjustments Credit	Adjusted Trial Balance Debit	Adjusted Trial Balance Credit	Income Statement Debit	Income Statement Credit	Balance Sheet & Statement of Changes in Equity Debit	Balance Sheet & Statement of Changes in Equity Credit
Cash	15				15				15	
Accounts receivable	22				22				22	
Supplies	25			8	17				17	
Ed Wolt, capital		40				40				40
Ed Wolt, withdrawals	12				12				12	
Service Revenue		48				48		48		
Supplies expense	14	—	8		22		22			
Totals	88	88	8	8			22	48	66	40
							26			26
Profit							48	48	69	96

Chapter 4

Quick Study 4-5

Account	(1) Temporary?	(1) Permanent?	(2) Financial Statement?
a. Accounts Payable		✓	
b. Insurance Expense	✓		
c. Delivery Vehicle		✓	
d. Interest Income	✓		
e. Unearned Revenue		✓	
f. Accumulated Depreciation		✓	
g. Stephos Petridis, Capital		✓	
h. Depreciation Expense	✓		
i. Stephos Petridis, withdrawals	✓		
j. Wages Payable		✓	
k. Prepaid Insurance		✓	
l. Utility Expense	✓		
m. Building		✓	
n. Supplies Expense	✓		

Quick Study 4-6

a. _____ 14000
   _____ + 13200
   _____
   _____
   _____
   _____
   _____

b. _____
   _____
   _____
   _____
   _____
   _____

Name: _____

Quick Study 4-7

Page____

Date	Account Titles and Explanation	PR	Debit	Credit
April 30	revenue		100	
	income Summary			100
	income Summary		60	
	expense			60
	income summary		40	
	Capital			40
	Capital		20	
	withdrawls			20

Assets

250	

Capital

20	200
	40

Revenue

100	100

Liabilities

	30

Withdrawals

20	20

Expenses

60	60

Income Summary

60	100
40	40

Name: _____

Quick Study 4-8

GENERAL JOURNAL

Page____

Date	Account Titles and Explanation	PR	Debit	Credit

Assets

250 |

Capital

| 200

Revenue

| 100

Liabilities

| 110

Withdrawals

20 |

Expenses

140 |

Income Summary

Quick Study 4-9

Post-Closing Trial Balance	Debit	Credit

Quick Study 4-10

a. _____ Preparing the unadjusted trial balance.
b. _____ Preparing the post-closing trial balance.
c. _____ Journalizing and posting adjusting entries.
d. _____ Journalizing and posting closing entries.
e. _____ Preparing the financial statements.
f. _____ Journalizing transactions.
g. _____ Posting the transaction entries.
h. _____ Completing the work sheet.

Quick Study 4-11

1. _____ Store equipment
2. _____ Wages payable
3. _____ Cash
4. _____ Notes payable (due in three years)
5. _____ Land not currently used in business operations
6. _____ Accounts receivable
7. _____ Trademarks

Name: _____

Quick Study 4-12

1. _____ Depreciation expense, trucks
2. _____ Lee Hale, capital
3. _____ Interest receivable
4. _____ Lee Hale, withdrawals
5. _____ Automobiles
6. _____ Notes payable (due in 3 years)
7. _____ Accounts payable
8. _____ Prepaid insurance
9. _____ Land not currently used in business operations
10. _____ Unearned services revenue
11. _____ Accum. deprec., trucks
12. _____ Cash
13. _____ Building
14. _____ Brand name
15. _____ Office equipment
16. _____ Land (used in operations)
17. _____ Repairs expense
18. _____ Prepaid property taxes
19. _____ Notes payable (due in 2 months)
20. _____ Notes receivable (due in 2 years)

Quick Study 4-13

Partial Balance Sheet		

*Quick Study 4-14

Name: _____

Quick Study 4-15

_____
_____
_____
_____
_____
_____
_____
_____
_____
_____

Quick Study 4-16

	2017	2016
Debt to equity ratio		

Comments: _____
_____
_____
_____
_____

*Quick Study 4-17

GENERAL JOURNAL   Page____

Date	Account Titles and Explanation	PR	Debit	Credit

Exercise 4-1

1. _____	Roberta Jefferson, withdrawals		9. _____	Cash
2. _____	Interest income		10. _____	Office supplies
3. _____	Accum. deprec., machinery		11. _____	Roberta Jefferson, capital
4. _____	Service revenue		12. _____	Wages payable
5. _____	Accounts receivable		13. _____	Machinery
6. _____	Rent expense		14. _____	Insurance expense
7. _____	Deprec. exp., machinery		15. _____	Interest expense
8. _____	Accounts payable		16. _____	Interest receivable

Exercise 4-2

ACCOUNT	ADJUSTED TRIAL BALANCE Debit	ADJUSTED TRIAL BALANCE Credit	INCOME STATEMENT Debit	INCOME STATEMENT Credit	BALANCE SHEET AND STATEMENT OF CHANGES IN EQUITY Debit	BALANCE SHEET AND STATEMENT OF CHANGES IN EQUITY Credit
Cash	21,000					
Accounts receivable	8,200					
Trucks	48,000					
Accum. deprec., trucks		31,250				
Franchise	6,500					
Accounts payable		13,000				
Salaries payable		14,600				
Unearned revenue		2,450				
Bo Webber, capital		37,750				
Bo Webber, withdrawals	7,200					
Plumbing revenue		31,600				
Deprec. expense, trucks	12,100					
Salaries expense	17,800					
Rent expense	6,000					
Miscellaneous expense	3,850					
Totals	130,650	130,650				

Exercise 4-3

Parts 1, 2, and 3

Musical Sensations

Work Sheet

For Year Ended December 31, 2020

Account Title	Unadjusted Trial Balance		Adjustments		Adjusted Trial Balance		Income Statement		Balance Sheet and Statement of Changes in Equity	
	Debit	Credit	Debit	Credit	Debit	Credit	Debit	Credit	Debit	Credit
Cash	7,500									
Accounts receivable	14,200									
Office supplies	790									
Musical equipment	125,000									
Accum. dep., musical equip.		21,600								
Accounts payable		4,200								
Unearned performance rev.		12,400								
Jim Daley, capital		154,300								
Jim Daley, withdrawals	52,000									
Performance revenue		138,000								
Salaries expense	86,000									
Travelling expense	45,010									
Totals	330,500	330,500								

Chapter 4

Exercise 4-3 (concl'd.)

Part 4

_____

_____

_____

_____

_____

Jim Daley, Capital

Exercise 4-4

1(a) _____

2(a) <div align="center">**GENERAL JOURNAL**</div> Page____

Date	Account Titles and Explanation	PR	Debit	Credit

3(a)

_____

_____

_____

_____

_____

Owner's Capital

1(b) _____

2(b) <div align="center">**GENERAL JOURNAL**</div> Page____

Date	Account Titles and Explanation	PR	Debit	Credit

3(b)

_____

_____

_____

_____

Owner's Capital

Name: _____

Exercise 4-5

	Debit	Credit
Rent revenue		97,000
Salaries expense	35,000	
Insurance expense	4,100	
Dock rental expense	11,700	
Boat supplies expense	5,920	
Depreciation expense, boats	21,200	
Totals		
Profit		
Totals		

Closing Entries

GENERAL JOURNAL Page____

Date	Account Titles and Explanation	PR	Debit	Credit

Name: _____

Exercise 4-6

GENERAL JOURNAL

Page____

Date	Account Titles and Explanation	PR	Debit	Credit

Post-Closing Trial Balance

	Debit	Credit

*Fundamental Accounting Principles,*16ce, Working Papers

Name: _____

Exercise 4-7

GENERAL JOURNAL

Page____

Date	Account Titles and Explanation	PR	Debit	Credit

Exercise 4-8

Part 1

Adjusted Trial Balance

	Debit	Credit

Name: _____

Exercise 4-8 (concl'd.)

Explanation: _____
_____
_____
_____
_____
_____

Part 2. Closing entries:

GENERAL JOURNAL   Page____

Date	Account Titles and Explanation	PR	Debit	Credit

Part 3.

Nick Stilz, Capital

Name: _____

Exercise 4-9

GENERAL JOURNAL

Page_____

Date	Account Titles and Explanation	PR	Debit	Credit

Exercise 4-9 (concl'd.)

Posting to Accounts:

Assets		Liabilities	
Bal. Dec. 31 142,000		51,000 **Bal. Dec. 31**	

Marcy Jones, Capital		Marcy Jones, Withdrawals	
	71,800 **Bal. Dec. 31**	**Bal. Dec. 31** 38,000	

Services Revenue		Salaries Expense	
	103,000 **Bal. Dec. 31**	**Bal. Dec. 31** 27,000	

Rent Expense		Insurance Expense	
Bal. Dec. 31 9,100		**Bal. Dec. 31** 1,500	

Depreciation Expense		Income Summary	
Bal. Dec. 31 8,200			

Exercise 4-10

Post-Closing Trial Balance

	Debit	Credit

Exercise 4-11

1. _____

_____

2.

	GENERAL JOURNAL			Page____

Date	Account Titles and Explanation	PR	Debit	Credit

3.   Jozef Jones, Capital

_____

_____

_____

Exercise 4-12

a.

Account Title	Adjusted Trial Balance	
	Debit	Credit
Accounts payable		$ 31,000
Accounts receivable	$ 48,000	
Accumulated depreciation, equipment		9,000
Accumulated depreciation, truck		21,000
Cash	14,400	
Depreciation expense	3,800	
Equipment	19,000	
Franchise	21,000	
Gas and oil expense	7,500	
Intangible asset	7,000	
Interest expense	450	
Interest payable		750
Land not currently used in business operations	148,000	
Long-term notes payable		35,000
Notes payable, due February 1, 2021		7,000
Notes receivable	6,000	
Prepaid rent	14,000	
Rent expense	51,000	
Repair revenue		266,000
Repair supplies	13,100	
Repair supplies expense	29,000	
Truck	26,000	
Unearned repair revenue		12,600
Vic Sopik, capital		74,900
Vic Sopik, withdrawals	49,000	
Totals	$457,250	$457,250

Name: _____

Exercise 4-12 (concl'd.)

b. _____ **Vic Sopik, Capital** _____

Analysis component: _____

_____

_____

_____

Exercise 4-13   **Calculations:**

a. **Current assets =**

_____

_____

_____

b. **Property, plant and equipment =**

_____

_____

_____

c. **Intangible assets =**

_____

_____

d. **Non-current investments =**

_____

_____

e. **Total assets =**

_____

_____

_____

f. **Current liabilities =**

_____

_____

_____

g. **Non-current liabilities =**

_____

_____

h. **Total liabilities =**

_____

_____

_____

i. **Total liabilities and equity =**

_____

_____

Exercise 4-14

Sunshine Sushi			
Balance Sheet			
December 31, 2020			
Assets			
Current assets:			
Total current assets			
Non-current investments:			
Property, plant and equipment:			
Total assets			
Liabilities			
Current liabilities:			
Total current liabilities			
Non-current liabilities:			
Total liabilities			
Equity			
Total liabilities and equity..			

Balance Sheet			

Exercise 4-16

Balance Sheet			

Fundamental Accounting Principles, 16ce, Working Papers

313

Name: _____

Exercise 4-17

a. _____
_____
_____
_____
_____

b. Journalizing:

GENERAL JOURNAL   Page____

Date	Account Titles and Explanation	PR	Debit	Credit

c. _____

Unadjusted Trial Balance

	Debit	Credit

Name: _____

Exercise 4-17 (cont'd.)

b, d, g. Posting journal entries in (b), adjustments in (d), and closing entries in (g):

Cash	
Bal. Dec. 31/19 **2,000**	

Leda Svenson, Capital	
	17,100 Bal. Dec. 31/19

Accounts Receivable	
Bal. Dec. 31/19 **5,000**	

Leda Svenson, Withdrawals	
Bal. Dec. 31/19 **-0-**	

Tutoring Revenue	
	-0- Bal. Dec. 31/19

Prepaid Rent	
Bal. Dec. 31/19 **3,000**	

Rent Expense	
Bal. Dec. 31/19 **-0-**	

Office Equipment	
Bal. Dec. 31/19 **20,000**	

Depreciation Expense	
Bal. Dec. 31/19 **-0-**	

Accum. Deprec., Office Equip.	
	10,000 Bal. Dec. 31/19

Advertising Expense	
Bal. Dec. 31/19 **-0-**	

Unearned Revenue	
	2,900 Bal. Dec. 31/19

Income Summary

Name: _____

Exercise 4-17 (cont'd.)

d. Journalize adjustments:

GENERAL JOURNAL   Page____

Date	Account Titles and Explanation	PR	Debit	Credit

e. _____

Adjusted Trial Balance

	Debit	Credit

Name: _____

Exercise 4-17 (cont'd.)

f. Financial statement preparation:

Income Statement

Statement of Changes in Equity

Balance Sheet

Name: _____

Exercise 4-17 (concl'd.)

g. Journalize closing entries:

GENERAL JOURNAL

Page_____

Date	Account Titles and Explanation	PR	Debit	Credit

h. _____

Post-Closing Trial Balance

	Debit	Credit

*Fundamental Accounting Principles,*16ce, Working Papers

Name: _____

Exercise 4-18

1. Prepare journal entries:

GENERAL JOURNAL   Page____

Date	Account Titles and Explanation	PR	Debit	Credit

Exercise 4-18 (cont'd.)

2, 3 and 5. Post journal entries, adjusting entries and closing entries to the general ledger :

Ledger as of May 31 (using the T-account format):

Cash

Supplies

Prepaid Insurance

Printer

Laptop

Accum. Dep., Laptop

Accum. Dep., Printer

Accounts Payable

Unearned Tour Revenue

Wages Payable

Emily Lee, Capital

Emily Lee, Withdrawals

Name: _____

Exercise 4-18 (cont'd.)

Parts 2, 3, 5

Tour Revenue	Deprec. Expense, Laptop	Deprec. Expense, Printer

Wages Expense	Insurance Expense	Supplies Expense

Income Summary		

Name: _____

Exercise 4-18 (cont'd.)

3. Prepare adjusting entries:

GENERAL JOURNAL   Page____

Date	Account Titles and Explanation	PR	Debit	Credit

4. Financial statement preparation:

Income Statement

Exercise 4-18 (cont'd.)

Statement of Changes in Equity

Balance Sheet

Name: _____

Exercise 4-18 (concl'd.)

5. Journalize closing entries:

GENERAL JOURNAL

Page____

Date	Account Titles and Explanation	PR	Debit	Credit

6.

Post-Closing Trial Balance

	Debit	Credit

Name: _____

*Exercise 4-19

_____
_____
_____
_____
_____
_____
_____
_____
_____
_____
_____
_____
_____
_____
_____
_____
_____
_____
_____
_____
_____
_____
_____

Exercise 4-20

	2021	2020
Current Ratio		
Quick Ratio		

Comments:

_____
_____
_____
_____
_____
_____
_____
_____
_____
_____
_____

Exercise 4-21

	2021	2020
Debt to equity ratio		

Comments: _____

_____

_____

_____

_____

_____

_____

_____

_____

_____

_____

_____

_____

*Exercise 4-22

GENERAL JOURNAL   Page_____

Date		Account Titles and Explanation	PR	Debit	Credit

Name: _____

*Exercise 4-23

1. Adjusting entries:

GENERAL JOURNAL
Page____

Date		Account Titles and Explanation	PR	Debit	Credit

2. Subsequent entries without reversing:

GENERAL JOURNAL
Page____

Date		Account Titles and Explanation	PR	Debit	Credit

*Exercise 4-23 (concl'd.)

3. Reversing entries and subsequent entries:

GENERAL JOURNAL   Page_____

Date	Account Titles and Explanation	PR	Debit	Credit

Problem 4-1A

Parts 1, 2, and 3

Silva Rentals
Work Sheet
For Year Ended March 31, 2020

Account Title	Unadjusted Trial Balance		Adjustments		Adjusted Trial Balance		Income Statement		Balance Sheet and Statement of Changes in Equity	
	Debit	Credit	Debit	Credit	Debit	Credit	Debit	Credit	Debit	Credit
Cash	7,000									
Rent receivable	31,000									
Office supplies	2,250									
Notes receivable, due 2023	46,000									
Furniture	16,000									
Building	216,000									
Land	41,000									
Patent	9,600									
Accounts payable		13,750								
Long-term note payable		175,000								
Stephen Silva, capital		90,250								
Stephen Silva, withdrawals	92,000									
Rent revenue		328,800								
Office salaries expense	52,000									
Interest expense	5,250									
Advertising expense	14,600									
Janitorial expense	41,000									
Utilities expense	34,100									
Totals	607,800	607,800								

Problem 4-2A

Parts 1, 2, and 3

Trenton Consulting

Work Sheet

For Year Ended June 30, 2020

Account Title	Unadjusted Trial Balance		Adjustments		Adjusted Trial Balance		Income Statement		Balance Sheet and Statement of Changes in Equity	
	Debit	Credit	Debit	Credit	Debit	Credit	Debit	Credit	Debit	Credit
Cash	680									
Accounts receivable	2,900									
Prepaid rent	3,660									
Equipment	9,600									
Accounts payable		1,730								
Toni Trenton, capital		26,650								
Toni Trenton, withdrawals	6,880									
Consulting revenue		30,200								
Wages expense	24,920									
Insurance expense	1,620									
Rent expense	8,320									
Totals	58,580	58,580								

Name: _____

Problem 4-2A (concl'd.)

Part 4

_____   **Toni Trenton, Capital**
_____
_____
_____

Analysis component:

_____
_____
_____
_____
_____
_____

Problem 4-3A

Part 1

Challenger Construction

Work Sheet

For Year Ended September 30, 2020

Account Title	Unadjusted Trial Balance Debit	Unadjusted Trial Balance Credit	Adjustments Debit	Adjustments Credit	Adjusted Trial Balance Debit	Adjusted Trial Balance Credit	Income Statement Debit	Income Statement Credit	Balance Sheet and Statement of Changes in Equity Debit	Balance Sheet and Statement of Changes in Equity Credit
Cash	22,000									
Supplies	17,200									
Prepaid insurance	9,600									
Land not currently used	50,000									
Equipment	106,000									
Accum. deprec., equipment		40,500								
Copyright	6,000									
Accounts payable		8,100								
Interest payable										
Wages payable										
Long-term notes payable		50,000								
Chris Challenger, capital		71,000								
Chris Challenger, withdrawals	68,000									
Construction revenue		255,620								
Deprec. Expense, equipment										
Wages expense	96,000									
Interest expense	1,200									
Insurance expense										
Rent expense	26,400									
Supplies expense										
Business taxes expense	10,000									
Repairs expense	5,020									
Utilities expense	7,800									
Totals	425,220	425,220								

Name: _____

Problem 4-3A (cont'd.)

Part 2

Adjusting entries:

GENERAL JOURNAL

Page_____

Date	Account Titles and Explanation	PR	Debit	Credit
a.				
b.				
c.				
d.				
e.				
f.				

Name: _____

Problem 4-3A (cont'd.)

Part 2

Closing entries:

GENERAL JOURNAL   Page____

Date	Account Titles and Explanation	PR	Debit	Credit

Problem 4-3A (cont'd.)

Part 3

Income Statement

Statement of Changes in Equity

Name: _____

Problem 4-3A (concl'd.)

Balance Sheet			

Analysis component:

a. _____

_____

_____

b. _____

_____

_____

_____

Problem 4-4A

Part 1   **GENERAL JOURNAL**   Page____

Date	Account Titles and Explanation	PR	Debit	Credit

Name: _____

Problem 4-4A (concl'd.)

Part 2

Post-Closing Trial Balance		

Problem 4-5A

Income Statement		

Statement of Changes in Equity		

Problem 4-5A (concl'd.)

Balance Sheet			

Analysis component:

_____

_____

_____

_____

_____

_____

Name: _____

Problem 4-6A

		GENERAL JOURNAL			Page____

Date		Account Titles and Explanation	PR	Debit	Credit

Income Statement

Statement of Changes in Equity

Problem 4-7A (concl'd.)

	Balance Sheet			

Analysis component:

_____

_____

_____

_____

_____

Name: _____

Problem 4-8A

Part 1

GENERAL JOURNAL

Page____

Date		Account Titles and Explanation	PR	Debit	Credit

Name: _____

Problem 4-8A (cont'd.)

Part 2

	Debit	Credit
Adjusted Trial Balance		

Name: _____

Problem 4-8A (concl'd.)

Part 3

GENERAL JOURNAL

Page____

Date	Account Titles and Explanation	PR	Debit	Credit

Name: _____

Problem 4-9A

Income Statement

Statement of Changes in Equity

Problem 4-9A (concl'd.)

	Balance Sheet			

Analysis component:

_____
_____
_____
_____
_____
_____
_____

Name: _____

Problem 4-10A

Part 1

Income Statement		

Part 2

Nolan Apex, Capital

Problem 4-11A

Income Statement

Statement of Changes in Equity

Name: _____

Problem 4-11A (concl'd.)

	Balance Sheet			

Analysis component:

_____
_____
_____
_____
_____
_____
_____

Fundamental Accounting Principles,16ce, Working Papers

Name: _____

Problem 4-12A

Part 1

_____

_____

_____

_____

Wyett North, Capital

Part 2

	Balance Sheet		

Name: _____

Problem 4-12A (concl'd.)

Part 3

_____

_____

_____

_____

_____

_____

_____

_____

Analysis component:

_____

_____

_____

_____

_____

_____

_____

_____

Name: _____

Problem 4-13A

Part 1. Use either the balance column format or T-accounts; both are provided.

GENERAL LEDGER

Cash   ACCOUNT NO. 101

DATE	EXPLANATION	PR	DEBIT	CREDIT	BALANCE

Accounts Receivable   ACCOUNT NO. 106

DATE	EXPLANATION	PR	DEBIT	CREDIT	BALANCE

Office Supplies   ACCOUNT NO. 124

DATE	EXPLANATION	PR	DEBIT	CREDIT	BALANCE

Prepaid Insurance   ACCOUNT NO. 128

DATE	EXPLANATION	PR	DEBIT	CREDIT	BALANCE

Furniture   ACCOUNT NO. 160

DATE	EXPLANATION	PR	DEBIT	CREDIT	BALANCE

Accumulated Depreciation, Furniture   ACCOUNT NO. 161

DATE	EXPLANATION	PR	DEBIT	CREDIT	BALANCE

Chapter 4

Name: _____

Problem 4-13A (cont'd.)

Computer Equipment ACCOUNT NO. 167

DATE	EXPLANATION	PR	DEBIT	CREDIT	BALANCE

Accumulated Depreciation, Computer Equipment ACCOUNT NO. 168

DATE	EXPLANATION	PR	DEBIT	CREDIT	BALANCE

Accounts Payable ACCOUNT NO. 201

DATE	EXPLANATION	PR	DEBIT	CREDIT	BALANCE

Salaries Payable ACCOUNT NO. 209

DATE	EXPLANATION	PR	DEBIT	CREDIT	BALANCE

Sam Near, Capital ACCOUNT NO. 301

DATE	EXPLANATION	PR	DEBIT	CREDIT	BALANCE

Sam Near, Withdrawals ACCOUNT NO. 302

DATE	EXPLANATION	PR	DEBIT	CREDIT	BALANCE

Commissions Revenue ACCOUNT NO. 405

DATE	EXPLANATION	PR	DEBIT	CREDIT	BALANCE

Depreciation Expense, Furniture ACCOUNT NO. 610

DATE	EXPLANATION	PR	DEBIT	CREDIT	BALANCE

Name: _____

Problem 4-13A (cont'd.)

Depreciation Expense, Computer Equipment   ACCOUNT NO. 612

DATE	EXPLANATION	PR	DEBIT	CREDIT	BALANCE

Salaries Expense   ACCOUNT NO. 622

DATE	EXPLANATION	PR	DEBIT	CREDIT	BALANCE

Insurance Expense   ACCOUNT NO. 637

DATE	EXPLANATION	PR	DEBIT	CREDIT	BALANCE

Rent Expense   ACCOUNT NO. 640

DATE	EXPLANATION	PR	DEBIT	CREDIT	BALANCE

Office Supplies Expense   ACCOUNT NO. 650

DATE	EXPLANATION	PR	DEBIT	CREDIT	BALANCE

Repairs Expense   ACCOUNT NO. 684

DATE	EXPLANATION	PR	DEBIT	CREDIT	BALANCE

Telephone Expense   ACCOUNT NO. 688

DATE	EXPLANATION	PR	DEBIT	CREDIT	BALANCE

Name: _____

Problem 4-13A (cont'd.)

	Income Summary			ACCOUNT NO. 901	
DATE	**EXPLANATION**	**PR**	**DEBIT**	**CREDIT**	**BALANCE**

Part 1. Use either T-accounts or the balance column format; both are provided.

Cash   101

Accum. Deprec, Furniture   161

Computer Equipment   167

Accum. Deprec, Computer Equip   168

Accounts Payable   201

Accounts Receivable   106

Salaries Payable   209

Office Supplies   124

Sam Near, Capital   301

Prepaid Insurance   128

Sam Near, Withdrawals   302

Commissions Revenue   405

Furniture   160

Problem 4-13A (cont'd.)

Part 1. Use either T-accounts or the balance column format; both are provided.

Deprec. Exp, Furniture 610	Office Supplies Expense 650

Deprec. Exp, Computer Equip. 612	Repairs Expense 684

Salaries Expense 622	Telephone Expense 688

	Income Summary 901

Insurance Expense   637

Rent Expense   640

Name: _____

Problem 4-13A (cont'd.)

Part 2. Transactions for June:

GENERAL JOURNAL   Page____

Date	Account Titles and Explanation	PR	Debit	Credit

Name: _____

Problem 4-13A (cont'd.)

Part 2. Transactions for June (cont'd.)

GENERAL JOURNAL

Page_____

Date	Account Titles and Explanation	PR	Debit	Credit

Problem 4-13A (cont'd.)

Part 3. Adjusting entries:

GENERAL JOURNAL   Page____

Date	Account Titles and Explanation	PR	Debit	Credit

Part 4. Financial statements:

Income Statement

Name: _____

Problem 4-13A (cont'd.)

Statement of Changes in Equity

Balance Sheet

Name: _____

Problem 4-13A (concl'd.)

Part 5. Closing entries:

GENERAL JOURNAL

Page____

Date	Account Titles and Explanation	PR	Debit	Credit

Part 6

Post-Closing Trial Balance

	Debit	Credit

Name: _____

Problem 4-14A

a.

	2018	2017
Current ratio		
Quick ratio		
Debt to equity ratio		

b. Comments:

_____
_____
_____
_____
_____
_____
_____
_____
_____
_____
_____
_____
_____
_____

Name: _____

*Problem 4-15A

Part 1

		GENERAL JOURNAL			Page____

Date		Account Titles and Explanation	PR	Debit	Credit
a.					
b.					
c.					
d.					
e.					
f.					

*Problem 4-15A (concl'd.)

Part 2

GENERAL JOURNAL   Page_____

Date	Account Titles and Explanation	PR	Debit	Credit

Part 3

GENERAL JOURNAL   Page_____

Date	Account Titles and Explanation	PR	Debit	Credit

Problem 4-1B

Parts 1, 2, and 3

Daimler Tours

Work Sheet

For Year Ended July 31, 2020

Account Title	Unadjusted Trial Balance		Adjustments		Adjusted Trial Balance		Income Statement		Balance Sheet and Statement of Changes in Equity	
	Debit	Credit	Debit	Credit	Debit	Credit	Debit	Credit	Debit	Credit
Cash	9,100									
Accounts receivable	18,700									
Notes receivable	16,000									
Prepaid insurance	5,100									
Furniture	6,750									
Accounts payable		6,925								
Unearned tour revenue		12,430								
Jan Rider, capital		60,975								
Jan Rider, withdrawals	-0-									
Tour revenue		16,700								
Wages expense	41,380									
Totals	97,030	97,030								

Problem 4-2B

Parts 1, 2, and 3

Tucker Photographers
Work Sheet
For Year Ended December 31, 2020

Account Title	Unadjusted Trial Balance		Adjustments		Adjusted Trial Balance		Income Statement		Balance Sheet and Statement of Changes in Equity	
	Debit	Credit	Debit	Credit	Debit	Credit	Debit	Credit	Debit	Credit
Cash	9,100									
Accounts receivable	13,000									
Prepaid equipment rental	3,860									
Automobile	49,000									
Accum. deprec., automobile		-0-								
Accounts payable		1,920								
Unearned revenue		5,740								
Jim Tucker, capital		65,700								
Jim Tucker, withdrawals	2,600									
Service Revenue		8,400								
Deprec. Expense, automobile	-0-									
Equipment rental expense	4,200									
Totals	81,760	81,760								

Name: _____

Problem 4-2B (concl'd.)

Part 4

_____

_____

_____

_____

Jim Tucker, Capital

Analysis component:

_____

_____

_____

_____

_____

_____

_____

Problem 4-3B

Part 1

Webster Demolition Company

Work Sheet

For Year Ended June 30, 2020

Account Title	Unadjusted Trial Balance		Adjustments		Adjusted Trial Balance		Income Statement		Balance Sheet and Statement of Changes in Equity	
	Debit	Credit	Debit	Credit	Debit	Credit	Debit	Credit	Debit	Credit
Cash	4,500									
Supplies	8,200									
Prepaid insurance	7,300									
Equipment	72,000									
Accum. deprec., equipment		5,000								
Accounts payable		9,100								
Interest payable										
Wages payable										
Long-term notes payable		45,000								
Rusty Webster, capital		21,400								
Rusty Webster, withdrawals	2,100									
Demolition revenue		83,300								
Deprec. expense, equipment										
Wages expense	27,400									
Interest expense	1,100									
Insurance expense										
Rent expense	24,400									
Supplies expense										
Business tax expense	4,200									
Repairs expense	4,200									
Utilities expense	8,400									
Totals	163,800	163,800								

Name: _____

Problem 4-3B (cont'd.)

Part 2

Adjusting entries:

GENERAL JOURNAL

Date	Account Titles and Explanation	PR	Debit	Credit
a.				
b.				
c.				
d.				
e.				
f.				

Fundamental Accounting Principles, 16ce, Working Papers

Name: _____

Problem 4-3B (cont'd.)

Part 2

Closing entries:

GENERAL JOURNAL

Page_____

Date	Account Titles and Explanation	PR	Debit	Credit

Problem 4-3B (cont'd.)

Part 3

Income Statement

Statement of Changes in Equity

Problem 4-3B (concl'd.)

Balance Sheet			

Analysis component:

a. _____

_____

b. _____

_____

_____

Name: _____

Problem 4-4B

Part 1

GENERAL JOURNAL

Page____

Date		Account Titles and Explanation	PR	Debit	Credit

Part 2

Post-Closing Trial Balance

	Debit	Credit

Problem 4-5B

Income Statement

Statement of Changes in Equity

Name: _____

Problem 4-5B (concl'd.)

Balance Sheet			

Analysis component:

_____
_____
_____
_____
_____
_____
_____

Name: _____

Problem 4-6B

GENERAL JOURNAL   Page____

Date	Account Titles and Explanation	PR	Debit	Credit

Problem 4-7B

Income Statement

Statement of Changes in Equity

Problem 4-7B (concl'd.)

Balance Sheet			

Analysis component:

_____
_____
_____
_____
_____
_____
_____

Problem 4-8B

Part 1

GENERAL JOURNAL

Date	Account Titles and Explanation	PR	Debit	Credit

Name: _____

Problem 4-8B (cont'd.)

Part 2

Adjusted Trial Balance		
	Debit	**Credit**

Name: _____

Problem 4-8B (concl'd.)

Part 3

GENERAL JOURNAL   Page____

Date	Account Titles and Explanation	PR	Debit	Credit

Income Statement

Statement of Changes in Equity

Name: _____

Problem 4-9B (concl'd.)

Balance Sheet

Analysis component:

_____

_____

_____

_____

_____

_____

Chapter 4

Name: _____

Problem 4-10B

Part 1

Income Statement		

Part 2

_____

Grant Greenway, Capital

Name: _____

Problem 4-11B

Income Statement

Statement of Changes in Equity

*Fundamental Accounting Principles,*16ce, Working Papers

Problem 4-11B (concl'd.)

Balance Sheet			

Analysis component:

_____
_____
_____
_____
_____
_____
_____

Name: _____

Problem 4-12B

Part 1

_____

_____

_____

_____

Jan Delta, Capital

Part 2

Balance Sheet			

Name: _____

Problem 4-12B (concl'd.)

Part 3

_____
_____
_____
_____
_____
_____
_____

Chapter 4

Name: _____

Problem 4-13B

Part 1. Use either the balance column format or T-accounts; both are provided.

GENERAL LEDGER

Cash ACCOUNT NO. 101

DATE	EXPLANATION	PR	DEBIT	CREDIT	BALANCE

Accounts Receivable ACCOUNT NO. 106

DATE	EXPLANATION	PR	DEBIT	CREDIT	BALANCE

Office Supplies ACCOUNT NO. 124

DATE	EXPLANATION	PR	DEBIT	CREDIT	BALANCE

Prepaid Insurance ACCOUNT NO. 128

DATE	EXPLANATION	PR	DEBIT	CREDIT	BALANCE

Land ACCOUNT NO. 170

DATE	EXPLANATION	PR	DEBIT	CREDIT	BALANCE

Buildings ACCOUNT NO. 173

DATE	EXPLANATION	PR	DEBIT	CREDIT	BALANCE

Accumulated Depreciation, Buildings ACCOUNT NO. 174

DATE	EXPLANATION	PR	DEBIT	CREDIT	BALANCE

*Fundamental Accounting Principles,*16ce, Working Papers

Problem 4-13B (cont'd.)

Accounts Payable   ACCOUNT NO. 201

DATE	EXPLANATION	PR	DEBIT	CREDIT	BALANCE

Salaries Payable   ACCOUNT NO. 209

DATE	EXPLANATION	PR	DEBIT	CREDIT	BALANCE

Amy Young, Capital   ACCOUNT NO. 301

DATE	EXPLANATION	PR	DEBIT	CREDIT	BALANCE

Amy Young, Withdrawals   ACCOUNT NO. 302

DATE	EXPLANATION	PR	DEBIT	CREDIT	BALANCE

Storage Revenue   ACCOUNT NO. 401

DATE	EXPLANATION	PR	DEBIT	CREDIT	BALANCE

Depreciation Expense, Buildings   ACCOUNT NO. 606

DATE	EXPLANATION	PR	DEBIT	CREDIT	BALANCE

Salaries Expense   ACCOUNT NO. 622

DATE	EXPLANATION	PR	DEBIT	CREDIT	BALANCE

Problem 4-13B (cont'd.)

Insurance Expense — ACCOUNT NO. 637

DATE	EXPLANATION	PR	DEBIT	CREDIT	BALANCE

Equipment Rental Expense — ACCOUNT NO. 640

DATE	EXPLANATION	PR	DEBIT	CREDIT	BALANCE

Office Supplies Expense — ACCOUNT NO. 650

DATE	EXPLANATION	PR	DEBIT	CREDIT	BALANCE

Repairs Expense — ACCOUNT NO. 684

DATE	EXPLANATION	PR	DEBIT	CREDIT	BALANCE

Telephone Expense — ACCOUNT NO. 688

DATE	EXPLANATION	PR	DEBIT	CREDIT	BALANCE

Income Summary — ACCOUNT NO. 901

DATE	EXPLANATION	PR	DEBIT	CREDIT	BALANCE

Name: _____

Problem 4-13B (cont'd.)

Cash	101		Accounts Payable	201

Accounts Receivable	106		Amy Young, Capital	301

			Salaries Payable	209

Office Supplies	124		Amy Young, Withdrawals	302

Prepaid Insurance	128		Storage Revenue	405

Land	170		Deprec. Exp., Buildings	606

Buildings	173		Salaries Expense	622

Accum. Deprec., Buildings	174		Insurance Expense	637

			Equipment Rental Expense	640

Name: _____

Problem 4-13B (cont'd.)

Office Supplies Expense	650		Telephone Expense	688

Repairs Expense	684		Income Summary	901

Part 2. Transactions for July:

GENERAL JOURNAL   Page____

Date	Account Titles and Explanation	PR	Debit	Credit

Problem 4-13B (cont'd.)

Part 2. Transactions for July (cont'd.)

GENERAL JOURNAL

Page____

Date	Account Titles and Explanation	PR	Debit	Credit

Name: _____

Problem 4-13B (cont'd.)

Part 3. Adjusting entries:

GENERAL JOURNAL

Page_____

Date	Account Titles and Explanation	PR	Debit	Credit

Part 4

Income Statement

Statement of Changes in Equity

Balance Sheet

Name: _____

Problem 4-13B (concl'd.)

Part 5. Closing entries:

GENERAL JOURNAL

Page____

Date		Account Titles and Explanation	PR	Debit	Credit

Part 6

Post-Closing Trial Balance

	Debit	Credit

*Fundamental Accounting Principles,*16ce, Working Papers

Name: _____

Problem 4-14B

a.

	2017	2016
Current ratio		
Quick ratio		
Debt to equity ratio		

b. Comments:

_____
_____
_____
_____
_____
_____
_____
_____
_____
_____
_____
_____
_____

Name: _____

*Problem 4-15B (cont'd.)

Part 1

GENERAL JOURNAL

Page_____

Date	Account Titles and Explanation	PR	Debit	Credit

Name: _____

*Problem 4-15B (concl'd.)

Part 2

GENERAL JOURNAL   Page____

Date	Account Titles and Explanation	PR	Debit	Credit

Part 3

GENERAL JOURNAL   Page____

Date	Account Titles and Explanation	PR	Debit	Credit

Name: _____

Cumulative Problem

Part 1   **Echo Systems**

GENERAL JOURNAL   Page____

Date	Account Titles and Explanation	PR	Debit	Credit

Name: _____

GENERAL JOURNAL

Page____

Date	Account Titles and Explanation	PR	Debit	Credit

Name: _____

Cumulative Problem (cont'd.)

GENERAL LEDGER

Cash   **ACCOUNT NO. 101**

DATE	EXPLANATION	PR	DEBIT	CREDIT	BALANCE
2020 Dec. 31	Balance				89,090

Accounts Receivable   **ACCOUNT NO. 106**

DATE	EXPLANATION	PR	DEBIT	CREDIT	BALANCE
2020 Dec. 31	Balance				5,700

Computer Supplies   **ACCOUNT NO. 126**

DATE	EXPLANATION	PR	DEBIT	CREDIT	BALANCE
2020 Dec. 31	Balance				1,440

Prepaid Insurance   **ACCOUNT NO. 128**

DATE	EXPLANATION	PR	DEBIT	CREDIT	BALANCE
2020 Dec. 31	Balance				3,240

Prepaid Rent   **ACCOUNT NO. 131**

DATE	EXPLANATION	PR	DEBIT	CREDIT	BALANCE
2020 Dec. 31	Balance				2,250

Office Equipment   **ACCOUNT NO. 163**

DATE	EXPLANATION	PR	DEBIT	CREDIT	BALANCE
2020 Dec. 31	Balance				18,000

Accumulated Depreciation, Office Equipment   **ACCOUNT NO. 164**

DATE	EXPLANATION	PR	DEBIT	CREDIT	BALANCE
2020 Dec. 31	Balance				1,500

Cumulative Problem (cont'd.)

Computer Equipment   ACCOUNT NO. 167

DATE	EXPLANATION	PR	DEBIT	CREDIT	BALANCE
2020 Dec. 31	Balance				36,000

Accumulated Depreciation, Computer Equipment ACCOUNT NO. 168

DATE	EXPLANATION	PR	DEBIT	CREDIT	BALANCE
2020 Dec. 31	Balance				2,250

Accounts Payable   ACCOUNT NO. 201

DATE	EXPLANATION	PR	DEBIT	CREDIT	BALANCE
2020 Dec. 31	Balance				2,310

Wages Payable   ACCOUNT NO. 210

DATE	EXPLANATION	PR	DEBIT	CREDIT	BALANCE
2020 Dec. 31	Balance				800

Unearned Computer Services Revenue ACCOUNT NO. 236

DATE	EXPLANATION	PR	DEBIT	CREDIT	BALANCE
2020 Dec. 31	Balance				3,000

Mary Graham, Capital   ACCOUNT NO. 301

DATE	EXPLANATION	PR	DEBIT	CREDIT	BALANCE
2020 Dec. 31	Balance				144,000

Mary Graham, Withdrawals   ACCOUNT NO. 302

DATE	EXPLANATION	PR	DEBIT	CREDIT	BALANCE
2020 Dec. 31	Balance				14,400

Name: _____

Cumulative Problem (cont'd.)

Computer Services Revenue — ACCOUNT NO. 403

DATE	EXPLANATION	PR	DEBIT	CREDIT	BALANCE
2020 Dec. 31	Balance				52,200

Depreciation Expense, Office Equipment — ACCOUNT NO. 612

DATE	EXPLANATION	PR	DEBIT	CREDIT	BALANCE
2020 Dec. 31	Balance				1,500

Depreciation Expense, Computer Equipment — ACCOUNT NO. 613

DATE	EXPLANATION	PR	DEBIT	CREDIT	BALANCE
2020 Dec. 31	Balance				2,250

Wages Expense — ACCOUNT NO. 623

DATE	EXPLANATION	PR	DEBIT	CREDIT	BALANCE
2020 Dec. 31	Balance				6,200

Insurance Expense — ACCOUNT NO. 637

DATE	EXPLANATION	PR	DEBIT	CREDIT	BALANCE
2020 Dec. 31	Balance				1,080

Rent Expense — ACCOUNT NO. 640

DATE	EXPLANATION	PR	DEBIT	CREDIT	BALANCE
2020 Dec. 31	Balance				6,750

Computer Supplies Expense — ACCOUNT NO. 652

DATE	EXPLANATION	PR	DEBIT	CREDIT	BALANCE
2020 Dec. 31	Balance				5,430

Fundamental Accounting Principles, 16ce, Working Papers

Chapter 4

Name: _____

Cumulative Problem (cont'd.)

Advertising Expense   ACCOUNT NO. 655

DATE	EXPLANATION	PR	DEBIT	CREDIT	BALANCE
2020 Dec. 31	Balance				5,820

Mileage Expense   ACCOUNT NO. 676

DATE	EXPLANATION	PR	DEBIT	CREDIT	BALANCE
2020 Dec. 31	Balance				2,800

Repairs Expense, Computer   ACCOUNT NO. 684

DATE	EXPLANATION	PR	DEBIT	CREDIT	BALANCE
2020 Dec. 31	Balance				2,610

Charitable Donations Expense   ACCOUNT NO. 699

DATE	EXPLANATION	PR	DEBIT	CREDIT	BALANCE
2020 Dec. 31	Balance				1,500

Income Summary   ACCOUNT NO. 901

DATE	EXPLANATION	PR	DEBIT	CREDIT	BALANCE
2020 Dec. 31	Balance				

Name: _____

Cumulative Problem (concl'd.)

Part 2

		ECHO SYSTEMS		
		Post-Closing Trial Balance		
		December 31, 2020		

	Debit	Credit

*Fundamental Accounting Principles,*16ce, Working Papers

Chapter 5

Name: _____

Quick Study 5-1

	A	B	C	D	E
Net sales	14 000	102 000	68 000	540 000	398 000
Cost of goods sold	8000	64 000	31 000	320 000	215 000
Gross profit from sales	6000	38 000	37000	220 000	183 000
Operating expenses	9000	31 000	22000	261 000	106 000
Profit (loss)	L 3000	7000	15000	L 41 000	77000

Quick Study 5-2

a. Periodic

b. Perpetual

c. Perpetual

d. Periodic

e. Perpetual

Quick Study 5-3

a.

b.

Quick Study 5-4

a.

b.

Quick Study 5-5

a.

b.

c.

Chapter 5   Name: _____

Quick Study 5-5 (concl'd.)

GENERAL JOURNAL   Page____

Date	Account Titles and Explanation	PR	Debit	Credit

d. Oct 15 - Nov 1 = 17 Days

Accounts Payable   5000

Cash   5000

GENERAL JOURNAL   Page____

Date	Account Titles and Explanation	PR	Debit	Credit

Quick Study 5-6

GENERAL JOURNAL   Page____

Date	Account Titles and Explanation	PR	Debit	Credit
1	Merch inventory		1200	
	accounts payable			1200
14	accounts payable		1200	
	Cash			1200

Copyright © 2019 by McGraw-Hill Education Limited. All rights reserved.

410   *Fundamental Accounting Principles, 16ce, Working Papers*

Quick Study 5-6 (concl'd.)

GENERAL JOURNAL

Page_____

Date		Account Titles and Explanation	PR	Debit	Credit
	15	Merch inventory		3000	
		accounts payable			3000
	30	accounts payable		3000	
		Merch inventory			60
		Cash			2940

Quick Study 5-7

GENERAL JOURNAL

Page_____

Date		Account Titles and Explanation	PR	Debit	Credit
Aug.	2	Merch inventory		14000	
		accounts Payable			14000
	4	accounts payable		1500	
		Merch inventory			1500
	17	Accounts payable		12500	
		Cash			12500

Quick Study 5-8

GENERAL JOURNAL

Page_____

Date		Account Titles and Explanation	PR	Debit	Credit
Mar	5	Merch inventory		2000	
		Accounts payable			2000
		Acc. payable		200	
		Merch inv			200

Quick Study 5-8 (concl'd.)

GENERAL JOURNAL   Page____

Date		Account Titles and Explanation	PR	Debit	Credit
Mar	15	Accounts payable		1800	
		Merch inventory			36
		Cash			1764

Quick Study 5-9

a. _____

_____

b. _____

_____

GENERAL JOURNAL   Page____

Date		Account Titles and Explanation	PR	Debit	Credit
c.					
d.					

Quick Study 5-10

GENERAL JOURNAL

Date	Account Titles and Explanation	PR	Debit	Credit

Name: _____

Quick Study 5-11

GENERAL JOURNAL

Page____

Date	Account Titles and Explanation	PR	Debit	Credit

Quick Study 5-12

GENERAL JOURNAL

Page____

Date	Account Titles and Explanation	PR	Debit	Credit

Name: _____

Quick Study 5-12 (concl'd.)

GENERAL JOURNAL

Page_____

Date		Account Titles and Explanation	PR	Debit	Credit

Quick Study 5-13

GENERAL JOURNAL

Page_____

Date		Account Titles and Explanation	PR	Debit	Credit

Calculations:

_____

_____

_____

Name: _____

Quick Study 5-14

a. Classified Multi-Step

	Income Statement			

b. Single-Step

	Income Statement			

Quick Study 5-15

	(a)	(b)	(c)	(d)

Calculations:

_____

_____

_____

_____

_____

_____

_____

_____

Name: _____

Quick Study 5-16

_____
_____
_____
_____
_____
_____
_____
_____
_____

Quick Study 5-17

_____
_____
_____
_____
_____
_____
_____
_____
_____
_____
_____
_____

Quick Study 5-18

1.

a.

b.

c.

2.

Quick Study 5-19

*Quick Study 5-20

QS5-6 - Periodic **GENERAL JOURNAL** Page_____

Date		Account Titles and Explanation	PR	Debit	Credit

Name: _____

*Quick Study 5-20 (concl'd.)

QS5-7 - Periodic **GENERAL JOURNAL** Page____

Date		Account Titles and Explanation	PR	Debit	Credit

QS5-8 - Periodic **GENERAL JOURNAL** Page____

Date		Account Titles and Explanation	PR	Debit	Credit

*Quick Study 5-21

QS5-10 - Periodic　　　　　　**GENERAL JOURNAL**　　　　　　Page____

Date	Account Titles and Explanation	PR	Debit	Credit

QS5-11 - Periodic　　　　　　**GENERAL JOURNAL**　　　　　　Page____

Date	Account Titles and Explanation	PR	Debit	Credit

Name: _____

*Quick Study 5-21 (concl'd.)

QS5-12 - Periodic   **GENERAL JOURNAL**   Page_____

Date	Account Titles and Explanation	PR	Debit	Credit

*Quick Study 5-22   *Name* _____

Name: _____

*Quick Study 5-23

	(a)	(b)	(c)	(d)

Calculations:

_____
_____
_____
_____
_____

*Quick Study 5-24

GENERAL JOURNAL

Page____

Date	Account Titles and Explanation	PR	Debit	Credit

*Quick Study 5-25

GENERAL JOURNAL

Page____

Date	Account Titles and Explanation	PR	Debit	Credit

Name: _____

*Quick Study 5-26

GENERAL JOURNAL

Page_____

Date		Account Titles and Explanation	PR	Debit	Credit

*Quick Study 5-27

GENERAL JOURNAL

Page_____

Date		Account Titles and Explanation	PR	Debit	Credit

Name: _____

Exercise 5-1

	a	b	c	d	e
Sales	$ 208,800	$ 165,000	$ 73,800		
Cost of goods sold			41,600	303,000	205,600
Gross profit from sales	108,200				75,200
Operating expenses	91,600	93,000		106,000	
Profit (loss)		(31,000)	(5,900)	57,000	(28,400)

Exercise 5-2

GENERAL JOURNAL

Page____

Date		Account Titles and Explanation	PR	Debit	Credit

Name: _____

Exercise 5-3

GENERAL JOURNAL

Page_____

Date		Account Titles and Explanation	PR	Debit	Credit

Exercise 5-4

GENERAL JOURNAL

Date	Account Titles and Explanation	PR	Debit	Credit

GENERAL JOURNAL

Page____

Date	Account Titles and Explanation	PR	Debit	Credit

Exercise 5-5 (concl'd.)

GENERAL JOURNAL

Date	Account Titles and Explanation	PR	Debit	Credit

GENERAL JOURNAL

Page____

Date	Account Titles and Explanation	PR	Debit	Credit

Exercise 5-6 (concl'd.)

GENERAL JOURNAL

Page____

Date	Account Titles and Explanation	PR	Debit	Credit

Name: _____

Exercise 5-7

a.   **Entries journalized by Wilson Purchasing:**

GENERAL JOURNAL

Page_____

Date	Account Titles and Explanation	PR	Debit	Credit

b.   **Entries journalized by Happy Sales:**

GENERAL JOURNAL

Page_____

Date	Account Titles and Explanation	PR	Debit	Credit

Name: _____

Exercise 5-7 (concl'd.)

GENERAL JOURNAL

Page_____

Date	Account Titles and Explanation	PR	Debit	Credit

Analysis component:

_____
_____
_____
_____
_____
_____
_____
_____
_____
_____
_____
_____
_____
_____

Exercise 5-8

1.	6.
2.	7.
3.	8.
4.	9.
5.	10.

Name: _____

Exercise 5-9

Merchandise Inventory	Cost of Goods Sold

Analysis component:

_____
_____
_____
_____
_____
_____
_____
_____
_____
_____
_____

Exercise 5-10

a. _____
b. _____
c. _____
d. _____

Analysis component:

_____
_____
_____
_____
_____
_____
_____
_____

Name: _____

Exercise 5-11

	Company A		Company B	
	2020	**2019**	**2020**	**2019**
Sales	$263,000	$187,000		$48,500
Sales discounts	2,630		1,200	570
Sales returns and allowances		16,700	6,200	
Net sales		$168,950		$45,500
Cost of goods sold	157,100		57,700	
Gross profit from sales	$ 51,700		$ 49,100	$ 22,100
Selling expenses	18,620	19,700	25,700	
Administrative expenses	26,300		30,400	9,700
Total operating expenses		$ 47,400		
Profit (loss)		$ 15,100		$ 2,700
Gross profit ratio				

Calculations:

_____
_____
_____
_____
_____
_____
_____

Analysis component:

_____
_____
_____
_____
_____
_____
_____

Name: _____

Exercise 5-12

Income Statement

Analysis component:

_____

_____

_____

_____

_____

_____

_____

Exercise 5-13

Part a **GENERAL JOURNAL** Page____

Date	Account Titles and Explanation	PR	Debit	Credit

Exercise 5-13 (Continued)

Note: A work sheet is not required for this question. The following shows the adjusted balances.

Account	Unadjusted Trial Balance		Adjustments		Adjusted Trial Balance	
	Debit	Credit	Debit	Credit	Debit	Credit

Perdu Sales
Work Sheet
For Year Ended December 31, 2020

Account	Debit	Credit	Debit	Credit	Debit	Credit
Cash	8,000					
Merchandise inventory	9,800					
Prepaid selling expenses	8,000					
Store equipment	40,000					
Accumulated depreciation, store equipment		9,800				
Accounts payable		14,840				
Salaries payable		0				
Eldon Perdu, capital		25,360				
Eldon Perdu, withdrawals	3,600					
Sales		858,000				
Sales returns and allowances	33,000					
Sales discounts	8,000					
Cost of goods sold	431,000					
Sales salaries expense	94,000					
Utilities expense, store	12,600					
Depreciation expense, store equip.	-					
Other selling expenses	70,000					
Other administrative expenses	190,000					
Totals	908,000	908,000				
Profit						
Totals						

Exercise 5-13 (cont'd.)

Part b

<table>
<tr><td colspan="4" align="center">Income Statement</td></tr>
<tr><td></td><td></td><td></td><td></td></tr>
<tr><td></td><td></td><td></td><td></td></tr>
<tr><td></td><td></td><td></td><td></td></tr>
<tr><td></td><td></td><td></td><td></td></tr>
<tr><td></td><td></td><td></td><td></td></tr>
<tr><td></td><td></td><td></td><td></td></tr>
<tr><td></td><td></td><td></td><td></td></tr>
<tr><td></td><td></td><td></td><td></td></tr>
<tr><td></td><td></td><td></td><td></td></tr>
<tr><td></td><td></td><td></td><td></td></tr>
<tr><td></td><td></td><td></td><td></td></tr>
<tr><td></td><td></td><td></td><td></td></tr>
<tr><td></td><td></td><td></td><td></td></tr>
<tr><td></td><td></td><td></td><td></td></tr>
<tr><td></td><td></td><td></td><td></td></tr>
<tr><td></td><td></td><td></td><td></td></tr>
<tr><td></td><td></td><td></td><td></td></tr>
<tr><td></td><td></td><td></td><td></td></tr>
<tr><td></td><td></td><td></td><td></td></tr>
</table>

Analysis component:

Exercise 5-14

1.

2.

3.

*Exercise 5-15

	(a)	(b)	(c)
Purchases			
Purchase discounts			
Purchase returns and allowances			
Transportation-in			
Cost of goods purchased			
Beginning inventory			
Cost of goods purchased			
Ending inventory			
Cost of goods sold			

*Exercise 5-16   Name _____

	Company A		Company B	
	2020	2019	2020	2019
Sales	110,000	178,000	90,000	
Cost of goods sold:				
Merch. inventory (beginning)	8,700	27,300	8,875	6,000
Net cost of merchandise purchases	82,000			26,100
Merch. Inventory (ending)		(22,000)	(8,920)	(9,875)
Cost of goods sold	82,300	106,000		
Gross profit from sales			39,545	19,775
Operating expenses	26,000	54,000	27,000	
Profit (loss)	1,700	18,000		6,275
Gross profit ratio				

Analysis component:

_____

_____

_____

_____

*Exercise 5-17

	(a)	(b)	(c)
Invoice cost of merch. purchases	44,000	21,000	16,250
Purchase discounts	2,000		325
Purchase returns and allowances	1,500	750	550
Cost of transportation-in		1,750	2,000
Merchandise inventory (beginning)	4,500		3,500
Net cost of merchandise purchases	44,700	19,750	
Merchandise inventory (ending)	2,200	3,750	
Cost of goods sold		20,800	17,065

*Exercise 5-18

GENERAL JOURNAL   Page_____

Date	Account Titles and Explanation	PR	Debit	Credit

*Exercise 5-18 (cont'd.)

GENERAL JOURNAL

Page_____

Date	Account Titles and Explanation	PR	Debit	Credit

Name: _____

*Exercise 5-18 (concl'd.)

GENERAL JOURNAL

Page____

Date	Account Titles and Explanation	PR	Debit	Credit

Name: _____

*Exercise 5-19

GENERAL JOURNAL

Page_____

Date	Account Titles and Explanation	PR	Debit	Credit

Name: _____

*Exercise 5-20

<table>
<tr><th colspan="5">GENERAL JOURNAL</th><th>Page____</th></tr>
<tr><th colspan="2">Date</th><th>Account Titles and Explanation</th><th>PR</th><th>Debit</th><th>Credit</th></tr>
<tr><td></td><td></td><td></td><td></td><td></td><td></td></tr>
<tr><td></td><td></td><td></td><td></td><td></td><td></td></tr>
<tr><td></td><td></td><td></td><td></td><td></td><td></td></tr>
<tr><td></td><td></td><td></td><td></td><td></td><td></td></tr>
<tr><td></td><td></td><td></td><td></td><td></td><td></td></tr>
<tr><td></td><td></td><td></td><td></td><td></td><td></td></tr>
<tr><td></td><td></td><td></td><td></td><td></td><td></td></tr>
<tr><td></td><td></td><td></td><td></td><td></td><td></td></tr>
<tr><td></td><td></td><td></td><td></td><td></td><td></td></tr>
<tr><td></td><td></td><td></td><td></td><td></td><td></td></tr>
<tr><td></td><td></td><td></td><td></td><td></td><td></td></tr>
<tr><td></td><td></td><td></td><td></td><td></td><td></td></tr>
<tr><td></td><td></td><td></td><td></td><td></td><td></td></tr>
<tr><td></td><td></td><td></td><td></td><td></td><td></td></tr>
<tr><td></td><td></td><td></td><td></td><td></td><td></td></tr>
<tr><td></td><td></td><td></td><td></td><td></td><td></td></tr>
<tr><td></td><td></td><td></td><td></td><td></td><td></td></tr>
<tr><td></td><td></td><td></td><td></td><td></td><td></td></tr>
<tr><td></td><td></td><td></td><td></td><td></td><td></td></tr>
<tr><td></td><td></td><td></td><td></td><td></td><td></td></tr>
<tr><td></td><td></td><td></td><td></td><td></td><td></td></tr>
</table>

Name: _____

*Exercise 5-21

GENERAL JOURNAL

Page____

Date	Account Titles and Explanation	PR	Debit	Credit

*Exercise 5-22

GENERAL JOURNAL

Page____

Date	Account Titles and Explanation	PR	Debit	Credit

Fundamental Accounting Principles, 16ce, Working Papers

*Exercise 5-22 (concl'd.)

GENERAL JOURNAL   Page____

Date	Account Titles and Explanation	PR	Debit	Credit

*Exercise 5-23

GENERAL JOURNAL   Page____

Date	Account Titles and Explanation	PR	Debit	Credit

Name: _____

*Exercise 5-23 (concl'd.)

GENERAL JOURNAL

Page____

Date	Account Titles and Explanation	PR	Debit	Credit

*Exercise 5-24

a. Entries journalized by Wilson Purchasing:

GENERAL JOURNAL   Page_____

Date	Account Titles and Explanation	PR	Debit	Credit

b. Entries journalized by Happy Sales:

GENERAL JOURNAL   Page_____

Date	Account Titles and Explanation	PR	Debit	Credit

Name: _____

*Exercise 5-24 (concl'd.)

GENERAL JOURNAL   Page____

Date	Account Titles and Explanation	PR	Debit	Credit

Name: _____

*Exercise 5-25

a.

b.

c.

d. _____

Analysis component:

Name: _____

*Exercise 5-26

a. _____

b. _____

c. _____

Income Statement

Fundamental Accounting Principles, 16ce, Working Papers

Name: _____

*Exercise 5-27

GENERAL JOURNAL Page____

Date	Account Titles and Explanation	PR	Debit	Credit

*Exercise 5-28

GENERAL JOURNAL Page____

Date	Account Titles and Explanation	PR	Debit	Credit

Problem 5-1A

Part 1   **GENERAL JOURNAL**   Page_____

Date	Account Titles and Explanation	PR	Debit	Credit

Problem 5-1A (concl'd.)

GENERAL JOURNAL   Page____

Date	Account Titles and Explanation	PR	Debit	Credit

Part 2

a. _____

b. _____

c. _____

_____

Problem 5-2A

GENERAL JOURNAL   Page____

Date	Account Titles and Explanation	PR	Debit	Credit

Name: _____

Problem 5-2A (cont'd.)

GENERAL JOURNAL

Page_____

Date		Account Titles and Explanation	PR	Debit	Credit

Problem 5-2A (concl'd.)

GENERAL JOURNAL

Page____

Date	Account Titles and Explanation	PR	Debit	Credit

Analysis component:

_____
_____
_____
_____
_____
_____
_____
_____
_____
_____

Problem 5-3A

GENERAL JOURNAL

Date	Account Titles and Explanation	PR	Debit	Credit

Name: _____

Problem 5-3A (concl'd.)

| | GENERAL JOURNAL | | | Page____ |

Date	Account Titles and Explanation	PR	Debit	Credit

Name: _____

Problem 5-4A

Part 1

	GENERAL JOURNAL			Page____

Date	Account Titles and Explanation	PR	Debit	Credit

Problem 5-4A (concl'd.)

Part 2- Multiple-step

Income Statement		

Analysis component:

_____

_____

_____

_____

_____

_____

Problem 5-5A

Part 1 - Classified, multiple-step

Income Statement

Part 2 - Single-step

Income Statement

Name: _____

Problem 5-6A

a. _____

_____

b. _____

_____

c. _____

_____

_____

	Tank Tops	Pullovers	Yoga Pants
Sale price			
Cost			
Gross Profit			
Gross Profit %			

d. _____

_____

_____

_____

_____

Problem 5-7A

Part 1 – Classified, multiple-step

Income Statement			

Name: _____

Problem 5-7A (concl'd.)

Part 2 – Single-step

	Income Statement		

Analysis component:

_____
_____
_____
_____
_____
_____
_____
_____
_____

Name: _____

Problem 5-8A

Part 1 – Classified, multiple-step

Income Statement			

Part 2 – Multiple-step

Income Statement		

Name: _____

Problem 5-8A (concl'd.)

Part 3 – Single-step

Income Statement		

Analysis component:

_____

_____

_____

_____

_____

_____

_____

Name: _____

*Problem 5-9A

GENERAL JOURNAL

Page_____

Date	Account Titles and Explanation	PR	Debit	Credit

Name: _____

*Problem 5-10A

GENERAL JOURNAL

Page____

Date	Account Titles and Explanation	PR	Debit	Credit

Name: _____

*Problem 5-10A (concl'd.)

GENERAL JOURNAL   Page_____

Date	Account Titles and Explanation	PR	Debit	Credit

Name: _____

*Problem 5-11A

1. _____

_____

_____

_____

_____

_____

_____

_____

2. _____

_____

_____

_____

_____

_____

_____

_____

_____

_____

3. _____

_____

_____

_____

_____

_____

_____

_____

_____

_____

_____

_____

_____

Name: _____

*Problem 5-11A (concl'd.)

4. Multi-step

Income Statement

5. Single-step

Income Statement

Name: _____

*Problem 5-12A

Analysis and calculations:

*Problem 5-12A (concl'd.)

Income Statement

Name: _____

*Problem 5-13A

| | GENERAL JOURNAL | | | Page____ |

Date	Account Titles and Explanation	PR	Debit	Credit

*Problem 5-14A

GENERAL JOURNAL   Page_____

Date	Account Titles and Explanation	PR	Debit	Credit

Name: _____

*Problem 5-14A (concl'd.)

GENERAL JOURNAL

Page_____

Date	Account Titles and Explanation	PR	Debit	Credit

Name: _____

Problem 5-1B

Part 1

GENERAL JOURNAL

Page____

Date	Account Titles and Explanation	PR	Debit	Credit

Name: _____

Problem 5-1B (concl'd.)

GENERAL JOURNAL   Page_____

Date	Account Titles and Explanation	PR	Debit	Credit

Part 2

a. _____

b. _____

c. _____

_____

Problem 5-2B

GENERAL JOURNAL   Page_____

Date	Account Titles and Explanation	PR	Debit	Credit

Name: _____

Problem 5-2B (cont'd.)

GENERAL JOURNAL

Page____

Date	Account Titles and Explanation	PR	Debit	Credit

Name: _____

Problem 5-2B (concl'd.)

GENERAL JOURNAL   Page_____

Date	Account Titles and Explanation	PR	Debit	Credit

Analysis component:

_____
_____
_____
_____
_____
_____
_____
_____
_____
_____
_____
_____
_____
_____

Name: _____

Problem 5-3B

GENERAL JOURNAL

Page_____

Date	Account Titles and Explanation	PR	Debit	Credit

Name: _____

Problem 5-3B (concl'd.)

GENERAL JOURNAL

Page_____

Date	Account Titles and Explanation	PR	Debit	Credit

Analysis component:

_____

_____

_____

_____

_____

Name: _____

Problem 5-4B

Part 1

GENERAL JOURNAL

Page_____

Date		Account Titles and Explanation	PR	Debit	Credit

Name: _____

Problem 5-4B (concl'd.)

Part 2 – Multiple-step

Income Statement

Analysis component:

_____

_____

_____

_____

_____

_____

_____

Name: _____

Problem 5-5B

1. Classified, multiple-step

Income Statement			

2. Single-step

Income Statement		

Name: _____

Problem 5-6B

a. _____
_____
_____

b. _____
_____

c. _____
_____
_____

	Small Handbags	Medium Handbags	Large Handbags
Sale price			
Cost			
Gross Profit			
Gross Profit %			

d. _____
_____
_____
_____
_____
_____
_____
_____
_____

Name: _____

Problem 5-7B

Part 1 – Classified, multiple-step

Income Statement			

Part 2 – Single-step

Income Statement		

Analysis component:

_____

_____

_____

_____

Name: _____

Problem 5-8B

Part 1 – Classified, multiple-step

Income Statement			

Name: _____

Problem 5-8B (concl'd.)

Part 2 – Multiple-step

Income Statement			

Part 3 – Single-step

Income Statement			

Name: _____

*Problem 5-9B

GENERAL JOURNAL

Page____

Date		Account Titles and Explanation	PR	Debit	Credit

Name: _____

Problem 5-10B

GENERAL JOURNAL

Page_____

Date	Account Titles and Explanation	PR	Debit	Credit

Name: _____

*Problem 5-10B (concl'd.)

GENERAL JOURNAL

Page_____

Date	Account Titles and Explanation	PR	Debit	Credit

Chapter 5

Name: _____

*Problem 5-11B

1. _____
_____
_____
_____
_____
_____
_____
_____

2. _____
_____
_____
_____
_____
_____
_____
_____
_____
_____

3. _____
_____
_____
_____
_____
_____
_____
_____
_____
_____
_____
_____

Name: _____

*Problem 5-11B (concl'd.)

4. Multiple-step

Income Statement		

5. Single-step

Income Statement		

Chapter 5   Name: _____

*Problem 5-12B

Analysis and calculations: _____

_____

_____

_____

_____

_____

_____

_____

_____

_____

_____

_____

_____

_____

_____

_____

_____

_____

_____

_____

_____

_____

_____

_____

_____

_____

_____

_____

_____

_____

_____

_____

_____

_____

_____

_____

_____

_____

_____

_____

_____

Name: _____

*Problem 5-12B (concl'd.)

Income Statement

Name: _____

*Problem 5-13B

GENERAL JOURNAL
           Page____

Date	Account Titles and Explanation	PR	Debit	Credit

Name: _____

*Problem 5-13B (concl'd.)

GENERAL JOURNAL

Page____

Date		Account Titles and Explanation	PR	Debit	Credit

*Problem 5-14B

GENERAL JOURNAL

Page____

Date		Account Titles and Explanation	PR	Debit	Credit

Name: _____

*Problem 5-14B (concl'd.)

GENERAL JOURNAL

Page____

Date	Account Titles and Explanation	PR	Debit	Credit

Name: _____

Cumulative Prob. (Perpetual)

Part 1   Echo Systems

GENERAL JOURNAL

Page_____

Date	Account Titles and Explanation	PR	Debit	Credit

Cumulative Prob. (Perpetual)

Part 1   **Echo Systems (cont'd.)**

GENERAL JOURNAL

Page____

Date	Account Titles and Explanation	PR	Debit	Credit

Name: _____

Cumulative Prob. (Perpetual)

Part 1   **Echo Systems (cont'd.)**

GENERAL JOURNAL

Page____

Date	Account Titles and Explanation	PR	Debit	Credit

Name: _____

GENERAL JOURNAL   Page____

Date	Account Titles and Explanation	PR	Debit	Credit

Name: _____

Cumulative Prob. (Perpetual)

Part 2   Echo Systems (cont'd.)

GENERAL LEDGER

	Cash				**ACCOUNT NO. 101**
DATE	**EXPLANATION**	**PR**	**DEBIT**	**CREDIT**	**BALANCE**
2020 Dec. 31	Beginning Balance				89,090

Cumulative Prob. (Perpetual)

Part 2   Echo Systems (cont'd.)

Accounts Receivable – Alamo Engineering   ACCOUNT NO. 106.1

DATE	EXPLANATION	PR	DEBIT	CREDIT	BALANCE
2020 Dec. 31	Beginning Balance				-0-

Accounts Receivable – Buckman Services   ACCOUNT NO. 106.2

DATE	EXPLANATION	PR	DEBIT	CREDIT	BALANCE
2020 Dec. 31	Beginning Balance				-0-

Accounts Receivable – Capital Leasing   ACCOUNT NO. 106.3

DATE	EXPLANATION	PR	DEBIT	CREDIT	BALANCE
2020 Dec. 31	Beginning Balance				-0-

Accounts Receivable – Decker Co.   ACCOUNT NO. 106.4

DATE	EXPLANATION	PR	DEBIT	CREDIT	BALANCE
2020 Dec. 31	Beginning Balance				2,700

Accounts Receivable – Elite Corporation   ACCOUNT NO. 106.5

DATE	EXPLANATION	PR	DEBIT	CREDIT	BALANCE
2020 Dec. 31	Beginning Balance				-0-

Name: _____

Cumulative Prob. (Perpetual)

Part 2   Echo Systems (cont'd.)

Accounts Receivable – Fostek Co.   ACCOUNT NO. 106.6

DATE	EXPLANATION	PR	DEBIT	CREDIT	BALANCE
2020 Dec. 31	Beginning Balance				3,000

Accounts Receivable – Grandview Co.   ACCOUNT NO. 106.7

DATE	EXPLANATION	PR	DEBIT	CREDIT	BALANCE
2020 Dec. 31	Beginning Balance				-0-

Accounts Receivable – Hacienda, Inc.   ACCOUNT NO. 106.8

DATE	EXPLANATION	PR	DEBIT	CREDIT	BALANCE
2020 Dec. 31	Beginning Balance				-0-

Accounts Receivable – Images, Inc.   ACCOUNT NO. 106.9

DATE	EXPLANATION	PR	DEBIT	CREDIT	BALANCE
2020 Dec. 31	Beginning Balance				-0-

Cumulative Prob. (Perpetual)

Part 2   Echo Systems (cont'd.)

Merchandise Inventory   ACCOUNT NO. 119

DATE	EXPLANATION	PR	DEBIT	CREDIT	BALANCE

Computer Supplies   ACCOUNT NO. 126

DATE	EXPLANATION	PR	DEBIT	CREDIT	BALANCE
2020 Dec. 31	Balance				1,440

Prepaid Insurance   ACCOUNT NO. 128

DATE	EXPLANATION	PR	DEBIT	CREDIT	BALANCE
2020 Dec. 31	Beginning Balance				3,240

Prepaid Rent   ACCOUNT NO. 131

DATE	EXPLANATION	PR	DEBIT	CREDIT	BALANCE
2020 Dec. 31	Beginning Balance				2,250

Office Equipment   ACCOUNT NO. 163

DATE	EXPLANATION	PR	DEBIT	CREDIT	BALANCE
2020 Dec. 31	Beginning Balance				18,000

Cumulative Prob. (Perpetual)

Part 2   **Echo Systems (cont'd.)**

Accumulated Depreciation, Office Equipment   ACCOUNT NO. 164

DATE	EXPLANATION	PR	DEBIT	CREDIT	BALANCE
2020 Dec. 31	Beginning Balance				1,500

Computer Equipment   ACCOUNT NO. 167

DATE	EXPLANATION	PR	DEBIT	CREDIT	BALANCE
2020 Dec. 31	Beginning Balance				36,000

Accumulated Depreciation, Computer Equipment   ACCOUNT NO. 168

DATE	EXPLANATION	PR	DEBIT	CREDIT	BALANCE
2020 Dec. 31	Beginning Balance				2,250

Accounts Payable   ACCOUNT NO. 201

DATE	EXPLANATION	PR	DEBIT	CREDIT	BALANCE
2020 Dec. 31	Beginning Balance				2,310

Wages Payable   ACCOUNT NO. 210

DATE	EXPLANATION	PR	DEBIT	CREDIT	BALANCE
2020 Dec. 31	Beginning Balance				800

Cumulative Prob. (Perpetual)

Part 2   **Echo Systems (cont'd.)**

Unearned Computer Services Revenue   ACCOUNT NO. 236

DATE	EXPLANATION	PR	DEBIT	CREDIT	BALANCE
2020 Dec. 31	Beginning Balance				3,000

Mary Graham, Capital   ACCOUNT NO. 301

DATE	EXPLANATION	PR	DEBIT	CREDIT	BALANCE
2020 Dec. 31	Beginning Balance				145,860

Mary Graham, Withdrawals   ACCOUNT NO. 302

DATE	EXPLANATION	PR	DEBIT	CREDIT	BALANCE

Computer Services Revenue   ACCOUNT NO. 403

DATE	EXPLANATION	PR	DEBIT	CREDIT	BALANCE

Sales   ACCOUNT NO. 413

DATE	EXPLANATION	PR	DEBIT	CREDIT	BALANCE

Chapter 5

Name: _____

Cumulative Prob. (Perpetual)

Part 2   Echo Systems (cont'd.)

Sales Discounts   ACCOUNT NO. 414

DATE	EXPLANATION	PR	DEBIT	CREDIT	BALANCE

Sales Returns and Allowances   ACCOUNT NO. 415

DATE	EXPLANATION	PR	DEBIT	CREDIT	BALANCE

Cost of Goods Sold   ACCOUNT NO. 502

DATE	EXPLANATION	PR	DEBIT	CREDIT	BALANCE

Depreciation Expense, Office Equipment   ACCOUNT NO. 612

DATE	EXPLANATION	PR	DEBIT	CREDIT	BALANCE

Depreciation Expense, Computer Equipment   ACCOUNT NO. 613

DATE	EXPLANATION	PR	DEBIT	CREDIT	BALANCE

Wages Expense   ACCOUNT NO. 623

DATE	EXPLANATION	PR	DEBIT	CREDIT	BALANCE

Cumulative Prob. (Perpetual)

Part 2   Echo Systems (cont'd.)

Insurance Expense   ACCOUNT NO. 637

DATE	EXPLANATION	PR	DEBIT	CREDIT	BALANCE

Rent Expense   ACCOUNT NO. 640

DATE	EXPLANATION	PR	DEBIT	CREDIT	BALANCE

Computer Supplies Expense   ACCOUNT NO. 652

DATE	EXPLANATION	P.R.	DEBIT	CREDIT	BALANCE

Advertising Expense   ACCOUNT NO. 655

DATE	EXPLANATION	PR	DEBIT	CREDIT	BALANCE

Mileage Expense   ACCOUNT NO. 676

DATE	EXPLANATION	PR	DEBIT	CREDIT	BALANCE

Repairs Expense, Computer   ACCOUNT NO. 684

DATE	EXPLANATION	PR	DEBIT	CREDIT	BALANCE

Charitable Donations Expense   ACCOUNT NO. 699

DATE	EXPLANATION	PR	DEBIT	CREDIT	BALANCE

Cumulative Prob. (Perpetual)

Part 3   Echo Systems

ECHO SYSTEMS
Partial Work Sheet
For Three Months Ended March 31, 2021

Acct. No.	Account Title	Unadjusted Trial Balance		Adjustments		Adjusted Trial Balance	
		Dr.	Cr.	Dr.	Cr.	Dr.	Cr.
101	Cash						
106.1	Alamo Engineering Co.						
106.2	Buckman Services						
106.3	Capital Leasing						
106.4	Decker Co.						
106.5	Elite Corporation						
106.6	Fostek Co.						
106.7	Grandview Co.						
106.8	Hacienda, Inc.						
106.9	Images, Inc.						
119	Merchandise inventory						
126	Computer supplies						
128	Prepaid insurance						
131	Prepaid rent						
163	Office equipment						
164	Accum. deprec., office equipment						
167	Computer equipment						
168	Accum. deprec., computer equip.						
201	Accounts payable						
210	Wages payable						
236	Unearned computer services rev.						
301	Mary Graham, capital						
302	Mary Graham, withdrawals						
403	Computer services revenue						
413	Sales						
414	Sales discounts						
415	Sales returns and allowances						
502	Cost of goods sold						
612	Deprec. exp., office equipment						
613	Deprec. exp., computer equip.						
623	Wages expense						
637	Insurance expense						
640	Rent expense						
652	Computer supplies expense						
655	Advertising expense						
676	Mileage expense						
684	Repairs expense, computer						
699	Charitable donations expense						
	Totals						

Name: _____

Cumulative Prob. (Perpetual)

Part 4   **Echo Systems (cont'd.)**

	ECHO SYSTEMS		
	Income Statement		
	For Three Months Ended March 31, 2021		

Part 5

	ECHO SYSTEMS	
	Statement of Changes in Equity	
	For Three Months Ended March 31, 2021	

Fundamental Accounting Principles, 16ce, Working Papers

Cumulative Prob. (Perpetual)

Part 6   **Echo Systems (concl'd.)**

ECHO SYSTEMS			
Balance Sheet			
March 31, 2021			

Cumulative Prob. (Periodic)

Part 1   **Echo Systems**

Journal Entries

GENERAL JOURNAL   Page____

Date	Account Titles and Explanation	PR	Debit	Credit

Cumulative Prob. (Periodic)

Part 1   **Echo Systems (cont'd.)**

Date	Account Titles and Explanation	PR	Debit	Credit

Cumulative Prob. (Periodic)

Part 1   **Echo Systems (cont'd.)**

Date	Account Titles and Explanation	PR	Debit	Credit

Name: _____

Cumulative Prob. (Periodic)

Part 1   **Echo Systems (cont'd.)**

Date	Account Titles and Explanation	PR	Debit	Credit

Cumulative Prob. (Periodic)

Part 2   Echo Systems (cont'd.)

GENERAL LEDGER

Cash   ACCOUNT NO. 101

DATE	EXPLANATION	PR	DEBIT	CREDIT	BALANCE
2020 Dec. 31	Beginning Balance				89,090

Cumulative Prob. (Periodic)

Part 2   **Echo Systems (cont'd.)**

Accounts Receivable – Alamo Engineering   ACCOUNT NO. 106.1

DATE	EXPLANATION	PR	DEBIT	CREDIT	BALANCE
2020 Dec. 31	Beginning Balance				-0-

Accounts Receivable – Buckman Services   ACCOUNT NO. 106.2

DATE	EXPLANATION	PR	DEBIT	CREDIT	BALANCE
2020 Dec. 31	Beginning Balance				-0-

Accounts Receivable – Capital Leasing   ACCOUNT NO. 106.3

DATE	EXPLANATION	PR	DEBIT	CREDIT	BALANCE
2020 Dec. 31	Beginning Balance				-0-

Accounts Receivable – Decker Co.   ACCOUNT NO. 106.4

DATE	EXPLANATION	PR	DEBIT	CREDIT	BALANCE
2020 Dec. 31	Beginning Balance				2,700

Accounts Receivable – Elite Corporation   ACCOUNT NO. 106.5

DATE	EXPLANATION	PR	DEBIT	CREDIT	BALANCE
2020 Dec. 31	Beginning Balance				-0-

Cumulative Prob. (Periodic)

Part 2   Echo Systems (cont'd.)

Accounts Receivable – Fostek Co.   ACCOUNT NO. 106.6

DATE	EXPLANATION	PR	DEBIT	CREDIT	BALANCE
2020 Dec. 31	Beginning Balance				3,000

Accounts Receivable – Grandview Co.   ACCOUNT NO. 106.7

DATE	EXPLANATION	PR	DEBIT	CREDIT	BALANCE
2020 Dec. 31	Beginning Balance				-0-

Accounts Receivable – Hacienda, Inc.   ACCOUNT NO. 106.8

DATE	EXPLANATION	PR	DEBIT	CREDIT	BALANCE
2020 Dec. 31	Beginning Balance				-0-

Accounts Receivable – Images, Inc.   ACCOUNT NO. 106.9

DATE	EXPLANATION	PR	DEBIT	CREDIT	BALANCE
2020 Dec. 31	Beginning Balance				-0-

Merchandise Inventory   ACCOUNT NO. 119

DATE	EXPLANATION	PR	DEBIT	CREDIT	BALANCE
2020 Dec. 31	Beginning Balance				-0-

Computer Supplies   ACCOUNT NO. 126

DATE	EXPLANATION	PR	DEBIT	CREDIT	BALANCE
2020 Dec. 31	Beginning Balance				1,440

Cumulative Prob. (Periodic)

Part 2   **Echo Systems (cont'd.)**

Prepaid Insurance   ACCOUNT NO. 128

DATE	EXPLANATION	PR	DEBIT	CREDIT	BALANCE
2020 Dec. 31	Beginning Balance				3,240

Prepaid Rent   ACCOUNT NO. 131

DATE	EXPLANATION	PR	DEBIT	CREDIT	BALANCE
2020 Dec. 31	Beginning Balance				2,250

Office Equipment   ACCOUNT NO. 163

DATE	EXPLANATION	PR	DEBIT	CREDIT	BALANCE
2020 Dec. 31	Beginning Balance				18,000

Accumulated Depreciation, Office Equipment   ACCOUNT NO. 164

DATE	EXPLANATION	PR	DEBIT	CREDIT	BALANCE
2020 Dec. 31	Beginning Balance				1,500

Computer Equipment   ACCOUNT NO. 167

DATE	EXPLANATION	PR	DEBIT	CREDIT	BALANCE
2020 Dec. 31	Beginning Balance				36,000

Accumulated Depreciation, Computer Equipment   ACCOUNT NO. 168

DATE	EXPLANATION	PR	DEBIT	CREDIT	BALANCE
2020 Dec. 31	Beginning Balance				2,250

Cumulative Prob. (Periodic)

Part 2   Echo Systems (cont'd.)

Accounts Payable   ACCOUNT NO. 201

DATE	EXPLANATION	PR	DEBIT	CREDIT	BALANCE
2020 Dec. 31	Beginning Balance				2,310

Wages Payable   ACCOUNT NO. 210

DATE	EXPLANATION	PR	DEBIT	CREDIT	BALANCE
2020 Dec. 31	Beginning Balance				800

Unearned Computer Services Revenue   ACCOUNT NO. 236

DATE	EXPLANATION	PR	DEBIT	CREDIT	BALANCE
2020 Dec. 31	Beginning Balance				3,000

Mary Graham, Capital   ACCOUNT NO. 301

DATE	EXPLANATION	PR	DEBIT	CREDIT	BALANCE
2020 Dec. 31	Beginning Balance				145,860

Mary Graham, Withdrawals   ACCOUNT NO. 302

DATE	EXPLANATION	PR	DEBIT	CREDIT	BALANCE

Cumulative Prob. (Periodic)

Part 2   Echo Systems (cont'd.)

Computer Services Revenue   ACCOUNT NO. 403

DATE	EXPLANATION	PR	DEBIT	CREDIT	BALANCE

Sales   ACCOUNT NO. 413

DATE	EXPLANATION	PR	DEBIT	CREDIT	BALANCE

Sales Discounts   ACCOUNT NO. 414

DATE	EXPLANATION	PR	DEBIT	CREDIT	BALANCE

Sales Returns and Allowances   ACCOUNT NO. 415

DATE	EXPLANATION	PR	DEBIT	CREDIT	BALANCE

Purchases   ACCOUNT NO. 505

DATE	EXPLANATION	PR	DEBIT	CREDIT	BALANCE

Name: _____

Cumulative Prob. (Periodic)

Part 2   Echo Systems (cont'd.)

Purchase Returns and Allowances — ACCOUNT NO. 506

DATE	EXPLANATION	PR	DEBIT	CREDIT	BALANCE

Purchase Discounts — ACCOUNT NO. 507

DATE	EXPLANATION	PR	DEBIT	CREDIT	BALANCE

Transportation-In — ACCOUNT NO. 508

DATE	EXPLANATION	PR	DEBIT	CREDIT	BALANCE

Depreciation Expense, Office Equipment — ACCOUNT NO. 612

DATE	EXPLANATION	PR	DEBIT	CREDIT	BALANCE

Depreciation Expense, Computer Equipment — ACCOUNT NO. 613

DATE	EXPLANATION	PR	DEBIT	CREDIT	BALANCE

Wages Expense — ACCOUNT NO. 623

DATE	EXPLANATION	PR	DEBIT	CREDIT	BALANCE

Cumulative Prob. (Periodic)

Part 2   **Echo Systems (cont'd.)**

Insurance Expense   ACCOUNT NO. 637

DATE	EXPLANATION	PR	DEBIT	CREDIT	BALANCE

Rent Expense   ACCOUNT NO. 640

DATE	EXPLANATION	PR	DEBIT	CREDIT	BALANCE

Computer Supplies Expense   ACCOUNT NO. 652

DATE	EXPLANATION	PR	DEBIT	CREDIT	BALANCE

Advertising Expense   ACCOUNT NO. 655

DATE	EXPLANATION	PR	DEBIT	CREDIT	BALANCE

Mileage Expense   ACCOUNT NO. 676

DATE	EXPLANATION	PR	DEBIT	CREDIT	BALANCE

Repairs Expense, Computer   ACCOUNT NO. 684

DATE	EXPLANATION	PR	DEBIT	CREDIT	BALANCE

Charitable Donations Expense   ACCOUNT NO. 699

DATE	EXPLANATION	PR	DEBIT	CREDIT	BALANCE

Name: _____

Cumulative Prob. (Periodic)

Part 3   Echo Systems (concl'd.)

ECHO SYSTEMS
Partial Work Sheet
March 31, 2021

Acct. No.	Account Title	Unadjusted Trial Balance		Adjustments		Adjusted Trial Balance	
		Debit	Credit	Debit	Credit	Debit	Credit
101	Cash						
106.1	Alamo Engineering Co.						
106.2	Buckman Services						
106.3	Capital Leasing						
106.4	Decker Co.						
106.5	Elite Corporation						
106.6	Fostek Co.						
106.7	Grandview Co.						
106.8	Hacienda, Inc.						
106.9	Images, Inc.						
119	Merchandise inventory						
126	Computer supplies						
128	Prepaid insurance						
131	Prepaid rent						
163	Office equipment						
164	Accum. deprec., office equipment						
167	Computer equipment						
168	Accum. deprec., computer equip.						
201	Accounts payable						
210	Wages payable						
236	Unearned computer services rev.						
301	Mary Graham, capital						
302	Mary Graham, withdrawals						
403	Computer services revenue						
413	Sales						
414	Sales discounts						
415	Sales returns and allowances						
505	Purchases						
506	Purchase returns and allowances						
507	Purchase discounts						
508	Transportation-in						
612	Deprec. exp., office equipment						
613	Deprec. exp., computer equip.						
623	Wages expense						
637	Insurance expense						
640	Rent expense						
652	Computer supplies expense						
655	Advertising expense						
676	Mileage expense						
684	Repairs expense, computer						
699	Charitable donations expense						
	Totals						

Parts 4, 5, and 6: Use the forms provided earlier.

Name: _____

Quick Study 6-1

1. _____
_____
_____

2. _____
_____
_____

Quick Study 6-2
_____
_____
_____
_____
_____

Quick Study 6-3
_____
_____
_____
_____
_____

Quick Study 6-4
_____
_____
_____
_____

Quick Study 6-5
_____
_____
_____
_____
_____
_____
_____
_____
_____

Quick Study 6-6

a. FIFO Perpetual

Date	Purchases	Sales (at cost)	Inventory Balance

b. Moving Weighted Average Perpetual

Date	Purchases	Sales (at cost)	Inventory Balance

Quick Study 6-7

Date	Purchases	Sales (at cost)	Inventory Balance

Quick Study 6-8

Date	Purchases/Transportation-In/(Purchase Returns/Discounts)			Cost of Goods Sold/(Returns to Inventory)			Balance in Inventory		
	Units	Cost Per Unit	Total $	Units	Cost Per Unit	Total $	Units	Avg Cost Per Unit	Total $
Jan. 1		BFWD					10	$15.00	$150.00
3				6					
7	25	$18.50	$462.50						
8			50.00						
17			(46.25)						
18				14					

Calculations:

Quick Study 6-9

a.

b.

c.

Quick Study 6-10

Parts a and b

Inventory Items	Units on Hand	Per Unit Cost	Per Unit NRV	Total Cost	Total NRV	LCNRV applied to: a. Inventory as a Group	LCNRV applied to: b. Each Product
Aprons	9	$6.00	$5.50				
Bottles	12	3.50	4.25				
Candles	25	8.00	7.00				

Part c   **GENERAL JOURNAL**   Page____

Date	Account Titles and Explanation	PR	Debit	Credit

Quick Study 6-11

a. _____
b. _____
c. _____
d. _____
e. _____
f. _____

Quick Study 6-12

_____
_____
_____
_____
_____
_____
_____
_____
_____
_____
_____
_____
_____
_____
_____
_____
_____
_____
_____

Quick Study 6-13

a. _____

_____

_____

_____

_____

_____

_____

_____

_____

b. _____

_____

Quick Study 6-14

_____

_____

_____

_____

_____

_____

_____

_____

_____

_____

_____

Quick Study 6-15

_____

_____

_____

_____

_____

_____

_____

_____

_____

_____

_____

Quick Study 6-16

_____

_____

_____

_____

_____

_____

_____

_____

Quick Study 6-17

a. Days' sales in inventory:

_____

_____

_____

_____

_____

_____

_____

_____

_____

b. Inventory turnover:

_____

_____

_____

_____

_____

_____

_____

_____

_____

*Quick Study 6-18

a. _____

_____

_____

b. _____

_____

_____

Exercise 6-1

	Include / Exclude?	Explanation and if applicable, correct inventory cost
a.		
b.		
c.		
d.		

Exercise 6-2

a. FIFO Perpetual

Date	Purchases	Sales (at cost)	Inventory Balance

Exercise 6-2 (cont'd.)

Gross profit calculation under FIFO:

_____
_____
_____
_____
_____
_____

b. Moving Weighted Average Perpetual

Date	Purchases	Sales (at cost)	Inventory Balance

Gross profit calculation under Moving Weighted Average:

_____
_____
_____
_____
_____
_____

Exercise 6-3

Specific Identification

Date	Purchases	Sales (at cost)	Inventory Balance

Gross profit calculation under Specific Identification:

Name: _____

Exercise 6-4

1. FIFO Perpetual

Date	Purchases	Sales (at cost)	Inventory Balance

2. Moving Weighted Average Perpetual

Date	Purchases	Sales (at cost)	Inventory Balance

Name: _____

Exercise 6-5

1. _____
_____
_____
_____
_____
_____
_____
_____

2. _____
_____
_____
_____
_____
_____

3(a). FIFO Perpetual

Date	Purchases	Sales (at cost)	Inventory Balance

Exercise 6-5 (concl'd.)

3(b). Moving Weighted Average Perpetual

Date	Purchases	Sales (at cost)	Inventory Balance

Exercise 6-6

Specific Identification

Date	Purchases	Sales (at cost)	Inventory Balance

Exercise 6-7

		Car Armour	
		Income Statements	
		For the Year Ended December 31, 2020	
	FIFO	Moving Weighted Average	Specific Identification

1. _____

2. _____
_____

Exercise 6-8

1.

July 1	21 units	@	$46	=	
July 3	66 units	@	51	=	
July 6	116 units	@	56	=	
July 23	<u>62 units</u>	@	56	=	
Totals	<u>units</u>				

      available for   cost of goods
      sale   available for sale

2.
Units sold:
    July 17   61 units
    July 31   <u>152 units</u>
     Totals   <u>units</u>

Therefore, units remaining in ending inventory:
        units available for sale
        units sold
        units remaining in ending inventory

Name: _____

Exercise 6-8

3a. FIFO

Date	Purchases			Sales (at cost)			Inventory Balance		
	Units	Unit Cost	Total Cost	Units	Unit Cost	Cost of Goods Sold	Units	Cost	Total Cost
July 1	21 @	$46							
July 3	66 @	$51							
July 6	116 @	$56							
July 17									
July 23	62 @	$56							
July 31									
Total									
	Cost of goods available for sale =			Cost of goods sold +			Ending inventory		

Name: _____

Exercise 6-8

3b. Moving Weighted Average

Date	Purchases			Sales (at cost)			Inventory Balance		
	Units	Unit Cost	Total Cost	Units	Unit Cost	Cost of Goods Sold	Units	Cost	Total Co
July 1	21 @	$46							
July 3	66 @	$51							
July 6	116 @	$56							
July 17									
July 23	62 @	$56							
July 31									
Total									
	Cost of goods available for sale =			*Cost of goods sold* +			*Ending inventory*		

Fundamental Accounting Principles, 16ce, Working Papers

Exercise 6-9

Date	Purchases/Transportation-In/(Purchase Returns/Discounts) Units	Cost Per Unit	Total $	Cost of Goods Sold/(Returns to Inventory) Units	Cost Per Unit	Total $	Balance in Inventory Units	AvgCost Per Unit	Total $
Mar. 1		BFWD					60	$94.00	$5,640.00
2	35	$96.00							
3				22					
4				(2)					
7				65					
17	40	97.00							
28				43					
Totals									

Calculations:

_____

_____

_____

_____

Analysis component:

_____

_____

_____

Exercise 6-10

Parts a and b

Inventory Items	Units on Hand	Per Unit Cost	NRV	Total Cost	Total NRV	LCNRV applied to: a. Inventory as a Group	b. Each Product
BB	27	$115	$120				
FM	10	150	143				
MB	41	191	177				
SL	45	83	97				

Part c

GENERAL JOURNAL Page____

Date	Account Titles and Explanation	PR	Debit	Credit

Exercise 6-11

1. _____

_____

_____

2.

For years ended December 31, 2020, 2021, and 2022 Income statement information should have been reported as:	Income statement information actually reported for years ended December 31,		
	2020	2021	2022
Sales			
Cost of goods sold:			
Beginning inventory			
+ Purchases			
– Ending inventory			
= Cost of goods sold			
Gross profit			

Name: _____

Exercise 6-12

_____
_____
_____
_____
_____
_____
_____
_____
_____
_____
_____
_____

Exercise 6-13

	At Cost	*At Retail*

Exercise 6-14

a. Estimated cost of physical inventory:

_____
_____
_____

b. Shrinkage at cost and at retail:

	At Cost	At Retail

Exercise 6-15

Name: _____

Inventory turnover (2021):

_____
_____
_____
_____

Inventory turnover (2020):

_____
_____
_____
_____

Days' sales in inventory (2021):

_____
_____
_____
_____

Days' sales in inventory (2020):

_____
_____
_____
_____

Comment on Russo's efficiency in using its assets to support increasing sales from 2020 to 2021.

_____
_____
_____
_____

Name: _____

*Exercise 6-16

	Ending Inventory	Cost of Goods Sold
a. FIFO Periodic:		

_____

_____

_____

_____

_____

b. Weighted Average Cost Periodic:

_____

_____

_____

_____

_____

Which method provides the lower profit and why?

_____

_____

*Exercise 6-17

	Ending Inventory	Cost of Goods Sold
a. FIFO Periodic:		

_____

_____

_____

_____

_____

b. Weighted Average Cost Periodic:

_____

_____

_____

_____

_____

Which method provides the lower profit and why?

_____

_____

Name: _____

*Exercise 6-18

_____
_____
_____
_____
_____
_____
_____
_____
_____
_____
_____
_____
_____
_____
_____
_____

Fundamental Accounting Principles, 16ce, Working Papers

Name: _____

Problem 6-1A

Part 1

	Include / Exclude?	Explanation and if applicable, inventory cost.
a.		
b.		
c.		
d.		
e.		

Part 2

Merchandise Inventory	
Unadjusted Balance.	
Adjusted Bal.	

Name: _____

Problem 6-2A

1a. FIFO Perpetual

Date	Purchases	Sales (at cost)	Inventory Balance

Problem 6-2A (cont'd.)

1b. Moving Weighted Average Perpetual

Date	Purchases	Sales (at cost)	Inventory Balance

Problem 6-2A (cont'd.)

2. Specific Identification

Date	Purchases	Sales (at cost)	Inventory Balance

3. GENERAL JOURNAL　　　　　　　　　　　Page_____

	Date	Account Titles and Explanation	PR	Debit	Credit
a.					
b.					

Problem 6-2A (concl'd.)

	GENERAL JOURNAL			Page____

Date	Account Titles and Explanation	PR	Debit	Credit
c.				

Name: _____

*Problem 6-3A

a. FIFO basis:

_____
_____
_____
_____
_____
_____
_____

b. Weighted Average basis:

_____
_____
_____
_____
_____
_____
_____
_____

Problem 6-4A

Calculation of cost of goods available for sale and units available for sale:

_____
_____
_____
_____
_____
_____
_____
_____
_____
_____
_____

Calculation of units in ending inventory:

_____
_____
_____
_____
_____
_____
_____

Fundamental Accounting Principles, 16ce, Working Papers

Problem6-4A (cont'd.)

1a. FIFO Perpetual

Date	Purchases	Sales (at cost)	Inventory Balance

1b. Moving Weighted Average Perpetual

Date	Purchases	Sales (at cost)	Inventory Balance

Problem 6-4A (concl'd.)

2.

	FIFO	Moving Weighted Average
Sales		
Cost of goods sold...................		
Gross profit		

Analysis component: _____

_____

_____

_____

_____

_____

*Problem 6-5A

a. FIFO basis:

_____

_____

_____

_____

_____

_____

_____

_____

_____

b. Weighted Average basis:

_____

_____

_____

_____

_____

_____

_____

_____

_____

Name: _____

Problem 6-6A

1a. FIFO Perpetual

Date	Purchases	Sales (at cost)	Inventory Balance

Problem 6-6A (cont'd)

1b. Moving Weighted Average Perpetual

Date	Purchases	Sales (at cost)	Inventory Balance

Part 2

	FIFO	Weighted moving average
Sales		
Cost of goods sold		
Gross Profit		

Part 3

_____
_____
_____
_____
_____
_____
_____

Name: _____

Problem 6-6A (concl'd.)

Part 4

_____
_____
_____
_____
_____
_____
_____

Name: _____

Problem 6-7A

1a. FIFO Perpetual

Date	Purchases			Sales (at cost)			Inventory Balance	
	Units	Unit Cost	Total Cost	Units	Unit Cost	Cost of Goods Sold	Units	Unit Cost
Jan. 1	Beginning inventory 295 @ $83.00 =							
Mar. 10	210 @ $87.00 =							
20								
May 13	277 @ $81.00 =							
Aug. 5	260 @ $67.00 =							
Sept 10								
Total								

Cost of goods available for sale = Cost of goods sold + Ending inve▮

Problem 6-7A (cont'd)

1b. Moving Weighted Average Perpetual

te	Purchases			Sales (at cost)			Inventory Balance		
	Units	Unit Cost	Total Cost	Units	Unit Cost	Cost of Goods Sold	Units	Unit Cost	Total Cost
1	Beginning inventory 295 @ $83.00 =								
10	210 @ $87.00 =								
20									
13	277 @ $81.00 =								
5	260 @ $67.00 =								
10									
tal									

Part 2

	FIFO	Weighted moving average
Sales		
Cost of goods sold		
Gross Profit		

Analysis component:

_____
_____
_____
_____
_____
_____
_____

Problem 6-8A

Fresh Express Company
Income Statement Comparing FIFO and Moving Weighted Average Cost
For Year Ended December 31, 2020

	FIFO	Moving Weighted Average
Sales		
Cost of goods sold		
Gross profit		
Operating expenses		
Profit		

Supporting calculations:

_____
_____
_____
_____
_____
_____
_____
_____
_____
_____
_____
_____
_____

Name: _____

Problem 6-8A (cont'd.)

a. FIFO Perpetual

Date	Purchases	Sales (at cost)	Inventory Balance

b. Moving Weighted Average Perpetual

Date	Purchases	Sales (at cost)	Inventory Balance

Problem 6-8A (concl'd.)

Analysis component:

_____
_____
_____
_____
_____
_____
_____
_____

*Problem 6-9A

	FIFO	Weighted Average
Fresh Express Company		
Income Statement Comparing FIFO and Weighted Average Periodic		
For Year Ended December 31, 2020		
Sales		
Cost of goods sold		
Gross profit		
Operating expenses		
Profit		

Supporting calculations:

_____
_____
_____
_____
_____
_____
_____
_____
_____
_____
_____
_____
_____
_____
_____

Problem 6-10A

Part 1

a. Cost of Goods Sold:	*2020*	*2021*	*2022*
Reported	_____	_____	_____
Adjustments: 12/31/2020 error	_____	_____	_____
12/31/2021 error	_____	_____	_____
Corrected	_____	_____	_____

b. Profit:	*2020*	*2021*	*2022*
Reported	_____	_____	_____
Adjustments: 12/31/2020 error	_____	_____	_____
12/31/2021 error	_____	_____	_____
Corrected	_____	_____	_____

c. Total Current Assets:	*2020*	*2021*	*2022*
Reported	_____	_____	_____
Adjustments: 12/31/2020 error	_____	_____	_____
12/31/2021 error	_____	_____	_____
Corrected	_____	_____	_____

d. Equity:	*2020*	*2021*	*2022*
Reported	_____	_____	_____
Adjustments: 12/31/2020 error	_____	_____	_____
12/31/2021 error	_____	_____	_____
Corrected	_____	_____	_____

Analysis component:

_____
_____
_____
_____
_____
_____
_____
_____
_____
_____
_____
_____
_____
_____
_____
_____

Name: _____

Problem 6-11A

	2020	2021	2022
Corrected Ending Inventory			
Corrected Cost of Goods Sold			
Corrected Profit			

Problem 6-12A

Part 1

Inventory Items	Units on Hand	Per Unit Cost	Per Unit NRV	Total Cost	Total NRV	LCNRV applied to: a. Major Group	b. Separately to Each Product
Audio equipment:							
Wireless audio receivers	332	$199	$188				
Touchscreen MP3 players	247	203	223				
Audio mixers	313	193	177				
Audio stands	191	85	103				
Subtotal							
Video:							
Televisions	467	253	298				
5GB video cards	278	171	183				
Satellite video recorders	199	613	618				
Subtotal							
Car Equipment:							
GPS navigators	172	171	145				
Double-DIN Car Deck with iPod/iPhone Control and Aux Input	157	213	198				
Subtotal							
Totals							

Problem 6-12A (concl'd)

2a.   **GENERAL JOURNAL**   Page____

Date		Account Titles and Explanation	PR	Debit	Credit

2b.   **GENERAL JOURNAL**   Page____

Date		Account Titles and Explanation	PR	Debit	Credit

Problem 6-13A

_____
_____
_____
_____
_____
_____
_____
_____
_____
_____
_____
_____
_____
_____
_____
_____
_____
_____
_____
_____
_____
_____
_____

Name: _____

Problem 6-14A

_____
_____
_____
_____
_____
_____
_____
_____
_____
_____
_____
_____
_____
_____
_____
_____
_____
_____
_____
_____
_____

Name: _____

Problem 6-15A

Part 1

	At Cost	At Retail
Earthly Goods		
Estimated Inventory		
December 31, 2020		

Part 2

	At Cost	At Retail
Earthly Goods		
Inventory Shortage		
December 31, 2020		

Name: _____

Problem 6-16A

Part 1

	At Cost	At Retail

Part 2

Problem 6-17A

	2018	2017
a. Inventory turnover ratio		
b. Days' sales in inventory		

Comments:

Name: _____

*Problem 6-18A

Part 1

_____
_____
_____
_____
_____
_____
_____
_____
_____
_____
_____
_____
_____
_____
_____
_____
_____
_____
_____
_____

Part 2

a. FIFO basis:

_____
_____
_____
_____
_____
_____
_____

b. Weighted Average basis:

_____
_____
_____
_____
_____
_____

Name: _____

Problem 6-1B

Part 1

	Include / Exclude?	Explanation and if applicable, inventory cost.
a.		
b.		
c.		
d.		
e.		

Part 2

Merchandise Inventory	
Unadjusted Balance.	
Adjusted Bal.	

Name: _____

Problem 6-2B

1a. FIFO Perpetual

Date	Purchases	Sales (at cost)	Inventory Balance

1b. Moving Weighted Average Perpetual

Date	Purchases	Sales (at cost)	Inventory Balance

Name: _____

Problem 6-2B (cont'd.)

2. Specific Identification

Date	Purchases	Sales (at cost)	Inventory Balance

Name: _____

Problem 6-2B (cont'd.)

3.   GENERAL JOURNAL   Page_____

Date	Account Titles and Explanation	PR	Debit	Credit
a.				
b.				
c.				

Chapter 6   Name: _____

*Problem 6-3B

a. FIFO basis:

_____
_____
_____
_____
_____
_____
_____

b. Weighted Average basis:

_____
_____
_____
_____
_____
_____

Name: _____

Problem 6-4B

1a. FIFO Perpetual

Date	Purchases	Sales (at cost)	Inventory Balance

1b. Moving Weighted Average Perpetual

Date	Purchases	Sales (at cost)	Inventory Balance

Name: _____

Problem 6-4B (concl'd.)

2.

	FIFO	Moving Weighted Average
Sales		
Cost of goods sold....................		
Gross profit		

Analysis component: _____

_____

_____

_____

_____

_____

*Problem 6-5B

a. FIFO basis:

_____

_____

_____

_____

_____

_____

_____

b. Weighted Average basis:

_____

_____

_____

_____

_____

_____

_____

_____

Fundamental Accounting Principles, 16ce, Working Papers

Name: _____

Problem 6-6B

1a. FIFO Perpetual

Date	Purchases	Sales (at cost)	Inventory Balance

Problem 6-6B (cont'd.)

1b. Moving Weighted Average Perpetual

Date	Purchases	Sales (at cost)	Inventory Balance

Part 2

	FIFO	Weighted moving average
Sales		
Cost of goods sold		
Gross Profit		

Part 3

Name: _____

Problem 6-6B (concl'd.)

Part 4

_____

_____

_____

_____

_____

_____

_____

Name: _____

Problem 6-7B

1a. FIFO Perpetual

Date		Purchases			Sales (at cost)			Inventory Balance	
	Units	**Unit Cost**	**Total Cost**	**Units**	**Unit Cost**	**Cost of Goods Sold**	**Units**	**Unit Cost**
Jan. 1	Beginning inventory 290 @ $82.00 =							
Mar. 10	205 @ $86.00 =							
20								
Apr. 30	281 @ $80.00 =							
July 5	255 @ $66.00 =							
Sep. 15								
Total								

Cost of goods available for sale   = Cost of goods sold   +   Ending inve

Problem 6-7B (cont'd)
1b. Moving Weighted Average Perpetual

te	Purchases			Sales (at cost)			Inventory Balance		
	Units	Unit Cost	Total Cost	Units	Unit Cost	Cost of Goods Sold	Units	Unit Cost	*Total Cost*
1	Beginning inventory 290 @ $82.00 =								
10	205 @ $86.00 =								
20									
30	281 @ $80.00 =								
5	255 @ $66.00 =								
15									
tal									

Part 2

	FIFO	Weighted moving average
Sales		
Cost of goods sold		
Gross Profit		

Analysis component:

_____
_____
_____
_____
_____
_____
_____

Problem 6-8B

Blizzard Company
Income Statement Comparing FIFO and Moving Weighted Average Cost
For Year Ended December 31, 2020

	FIFO	Moving Weighted Average
Sales		
Cost of goods sold		
Gross profit		
Operating expenses		
Profit		

Supporting calculations:

_____
_____
_____
_____
_____
_____
_____
_____
_____
_____
_____
_____
_____
_____
_____
_____

Problem 6-8B (cont'd.)

a. FIFO Perpetual

Date	Purchases	Sales (at cost)	Inventory Balance

b. Moving Weighted-Average Perpetual

Date	Purchases	Sales (at cost)	Inventory Balance

Problem 6-8B (concl'd.)

Analysis component:

_____
_____
_____
_____
_____
_____
_____
_____
_____

Name: _____

*Problem 6-9B

Blizzard Company

Income Statement Comparing FIFO and Weighted Average Periodic

For Year Ended December 31, 2020

	FIFO	Weighted Average
Sales		
Cost of goods sold		
Gross profit		
Operating expenses		
Profit		

Supporting calculations:

_____
_____
_____
_____
_____
_____
_____
_____
_____

a. FIFO Periodic

_____
_____
_____
_____
_____
_____
_____
_____

b. Weighted Average Periodic

_____
_____
_____
_____
_____
_____
_____

Problem 6-10B

Part 1

a. Cost of Goods Sold:		*2020*	*2021*	*2022*
Reported..		_____	_____	_____
Adjustments:	12/31/2020 error	_____	_____	_____
	12/31/2021 error	_____	_____	_____
Corrected		_____	_____	_____

b. Profit:		*2020*	*2021*	*2022*
Reported..		_____	_____	_____
Adjustments:	12/31/2020 error	_____	_____	_____
	12/31/2021 error	_____	_____	_____
Corrected		_____	_____	_____

c. Total Current Assets:		*2020*	*2021*	*2022*
Reported..		_____	_____	_____
Adjustments:	12/31/2020 error	_____	_____	_____
	12/31/2021 error	_____	_____	_____
Corrected		_____	_____	_____

d. Equity:		*2020*	*2021*	*2022*
Reported..		_____	_____	_____
Adjustments:	12/31/2020 error	_____	_____	_____
	12/31/2021 error	_____	_____	_____
Corrected		_____	_____	_____

Analysis component:

_____

_____

_____

_____

_____

_____

_____

_____

_____

_____

_____

_____

_____

_____

_____

_____

Name: _____

Problem 6-11B

Part 1

	Incorrect Income Statement Information For Years Ended December 31				Corrected Income Statement Information For Years Ended December 31			
	2020	**%**	**2021**	**%**	**2020**	**%**	**2021**	**%**
Sales								
Cost of goods sold......								
Gross profit								

Part 2

_____

_____

_____

_____

Problem 6-12B

Part 1

Inventory Items	Units on Hand	Per Unit		Total Cost	Total NRV	LCNRV applied to:	
		Cost	NRV			a. Major Category	b. Separately to Each Product
Office furniture:							
Desks	430	$261	$305				
Credenzas	290	227	256				
Chairs	585	49	43				
Bookshelves	320	93	82				
Filing cabinets:							
Two-drawer	215	81	70				
Four-drawer	400	135	122				
Lateral	178	104	118				
Office Equip.:							
Fax machines	415	168	200				
Copiers	544	317	288				
Typewriters	355	125	117				

Problem 6-12B (concl'd)

2a. **GENERAL JOURNAL** Page_____

Date	Account Titles and Explanation	PR	Debit	Credit

2b. **GENERAL JOURNAL** Page_____

Date	Account Titles and Explanation	PR	Debit	Credit

Problem 6-13B

Problem 6-14B

_____
_____
_____
_____
_____
_____
_____
_____
_____
_____
_____
_____
_____
_____
_____
_____
_____
_____
_____
_____

Name: _____

Problem 6-15B

Part 1

	At Cost	At Retail
THE WILKE CO.		
Estimated Inventory		
December 31, 2020		

Part 2

	At Cost	At Retail
THE WILKE CO.		
Inventory Shortage		
December 31, 2020		

Fundamental Accounting Principles, 16ce, Working Papers

Problem 6-16B

Part 1

	At Cost	At Retail

Problem 6-17B

	2017	2016
c. Inventory turnover ratio		
d. Days' sales in inventory		

Comments: _____
_____
_____
_____
_____
_____
_____

Chapter 6

Name: _____

*Problem 6-18B

Part 1

_____
_____
_____
_____
_____
_____
_____
_____
_____

Part 2

a. FIFO basis:

_____
_____
_____
_____
_____

b. Weighted Average basis:

_____
_____
_____
_____
_____

Name: _____

Quick Study 7-1

(a) _____
_____
_____
_____
_____
_____
_____

(b) _____
_____
_____
_____
_____
_____
_____

(c) _____
_____
_____
_____

Quick Study 7-2

_____
_____
_____
_____
_____
_____
_____
_____
_____

Name: _____

Quick Study 7-3

Weakness #1	
Implication	
Recommendation	

Weakness #2	
Implication	
Recommendation	

Weakness #3	
Implication	
Recommendation	

Fundamental Accounting Principles, 16ce, Working Papers

Quick Study 7-4

(1) Establishment of the fund:

GENERAL JOURNAL   Page_____

Date		Account Titles and Explanation	PR	Debit	Credit

(2) Summary of petty cash receipts and entry to reimburse the fund at month-end:

Wee Ones Agency
Petty Cash Payments Report
May 1 – 31, 2020

Receipts:

Fund total
Less: Cash remaining
Equals: Cash required to replenish petty cash
Cash over/(short)

GENERAL JOURNAL   Page_____

Date		Account Titles and Explanation	PR	Debit	Credit

(3) _____

Name: _____

Quick Study 7-5

GENERAL JOURNAL Page____

Date	Account Titles and Explanation	PR	Debit	Credit

Quick Study 7-6

GENERAL JOURNAL Page____

Date	Account Titles and Explanation	PR	Debit	Credit

Name: _____

Quick Study 7-7

GENERAL JOURNAL

Page_____

Date	Account Titles and Explanation	PR	Debit	Credit

Quick Study 7-8

| | GENERAL JOURNAL | | | | Page_____ |

Date	Account Titles and Explanation	PR	Debit	Credit

Quick Study 7-9   Parts 1 and 2:

	Bank or Book Side	Add or Subtract	Journal Entry Required or Not
(a)			
(b)			
(c)			
(d)			
(e)			
(f)			
(g)			

Quick Study 7-10

	Bank Reconciliation		

GENERAL JOURNAL Page____

Date	Account Titles and Explanation	PR	Debit	Credit

Quick Study 7-11

Part A

Name: _____

Quick Study 7-11 (concl'd.)

Part B

GENERAL JOURNAL

Page_____

Date		Account Titles and Explanation	PR	Debit	Credit

Quick Study 7-12

_____
_____
_____
_____
_____
_____
_____
_____
_____
_____
_____
_____
_____
_____
_____
_____

Chapter 7

Exercise 7-1

_____
_____
_____
_____
_____
_____
_____
_____
_____
_____

Exercise 7-2

_____
_____
_____
_____
_____
_____
_____
_____
_____
_____
_____
_____
_____
_____
_____
_____
_____
_____
_____
_____
_____
_____
_____
_____
_____
_____
_____
_____

Exercise 7-3

(a) _____

_____

_____

_____

_____

_____

(b) _____

_____

_____

_____

_____

_____

_____

Name: _____

Exercise 7-4

Internal Control Problem: _____
_____
_____
_____
_____
_____
_____
_____

Internal Control Recommendation: _____
_____
_____
_____
_____

Exercise 7-5

(a) Establish the Fund

GENERAL JOURNAL   Page____

Date	Account Titles and Explanation	PR	Debit	Credit

(b) Prepare a summary of petty cash receipts

Cameron Co.
Petty Cash Payments Report
January 1 – 8, 2020

Receipts: _____

_____

_____

_____

_____

_____

Fund total

Less: Cash remaining

Equals: Cash required to replenish petty cash

Cash over/(short)

Name: _____

Exercise 7-5 (concl'd.)

Record the reimbursement:

GENERAL JOURNAL   Page____

Date	Account Titles and Explanation	PR	Debit	Credit

Analysis component: _____

_____

_____

_____

_____

Exercise 7-6

(a) Establish the Fund

GENERAL JOURNAL   Page____

Date	Account Titles and Explanation	PR	Debit	Credit

Exercise 7-6 (concl'd.)

(b) Prepare a summary of petty cash receipts

Willard Company
Petty Cash Payments Report
September 9 – 30, 2020

Receipts:
_____
_____
_____
_____
_____
_____

Fund total _____
Less: Cash remaining _____
Equals: Cash required to replenish petty cash ___
Cash over/(short) _____

Reimburse and reduce the fund

GENERAL JOURNAL   Page_____

Date	Account Titles and Explanation	PR	Debit	Credit

Analysis component:

_____
_____
_____
_____
_____
_____
_____

Exercise 7-7

GENERAL JOURNAL

Page_____

Date		Account Titles and Explanation	PR	Debit	Credit
a.					
b.					
c.					

Exercise 7-8

(a) Establish the Fund

GENERAL JOURNAL

Page_____

Date		Account Titles and Explanation	PR	Debit	Credit

Exercise 7-8 (concl'd.)

(b) Prepare a summary of petty cash receipts

Dallas Repairs
Petty Cash Payments Report
July 5– 31, 2020

Receipts:

_____

_____

_____

_____

_____

_____

Fund total

Less: Cash remaining

Equals: Cash required to replenish petty cash

Cash over/(short)

Reimburse and reduce the fund

GENERAL JOURNAL   Page____

Date		Account Titles and Explanation	PR	Debit	Credit

Analysis component:

_____

_____

_____

_____

_____

_____

_____

_____

GENERAL JOURNAL

Page____

Date	Account Titles and Explanation	PR	Debit	Credit

Name: _____

Exercise 7-10

GENERAL JOURNAL

Page_____

Date	Account Titles and Explanation	PR	Debit	Credit

Name: _____

Exercise 7-10 (concl'd.)

GENERAL JOURNAL   Page_____

Date		Account Titles and Explanation	PR	Debit	Credit

Analysis component:

_____
_____
_____
_____
_____
_____
_____
_____
_____
_____
_____
_____
_____
_____
_____
_____
_____
_____
_____
_____
_____
_____

Name: _____

Exercise 7-11

Part 1

_____

_____

Part 2

GENERAL JOURNAL

Page_____

Date		Account Titles and Explanation	PR	Debit	Credit

Analysis component: _____

_____

_____

_____

_____

_____

_____

Name: _____

Exercise 7-12

a. _____

_____

b. <div align="center">**GENERAL JOURNAL**</div> Page____

Date	Account Titles and Explanation	PR	Debit	Credit

Analysis component:

_____

_____

_____

_____

_____

_____

_____

Exercise 7-13

	Bank Balance		Book Balance			Not Shown on the Reconciliation
	Add	Deduct	Add	Deduct	Adjust	
1. Interest income earned on the account.						
2. Deposit made on September 30 after the bank was closed.						
3. Cheques outstanding on August 31 that cleared the bank in September.						
4. NSF cheque from customer returned on September 15 but not recorded by the company.						
5. Cheques written and mailed to payees on September 30.						
6. Deposit made on September 5 that was processed on Sept. 8.						
7. Bank service charge.						
8. Cheques written and mailed to payees on October 5.						
9. Cheque written by another company but charged against the company's account in error.						
10. Customer payment through electronic funds transfer received in the bank but not recorded in the company's books.						
11. Bank charge for collection of electronic fund transfer in Item 10.						
12. Cheque written against the account and cleared by the bank; not recorded by the bookkeeper.						

Name: _____

Exercise 7-14

	Case X	Case Y	Case Z

Name: _____

Problem 7-1A

(1) Principle Violated:

    Recommendation:

---

(2) Principle Violated:

    Recommendation:

---

(3) Principle Violated:

    Recommendation:

---

(4) Principle Violated:

    Recommendation:

---

(5) Principle Violated:

    Recommendation:

Name: _____

Problem 7-2A

Part 1   **GENERAL JOURNAL**   Page____

Date	Account Titles and Explanation	PR	Debit	Credit

Part 2

Halifax Fitness Consulting
Petty Cash Payments Report
February 2 – 28, 2020

Receipts:

Fund total

Less: Cash remaining

Equals: Cash required to replenish petty cash

Cash over/(short)

Part 3   **GENERAL JOURNAL**   Page____

Date	Account Titles and Explanation	PR	Debit	Credit

Problem 7-2A (concl'd.)

Analysis component: _____

_____

_____

_____

_____

_____

_____

_____

Problem 7-3A

GENERAL JOURNAL   Page____

Date		Account Titles and Explanation	PR	Debit	Credit

Analysis component: _____

_____

_____

_____

_____

_____

_____

GENERAL JOURNAL

Page____

Date	Account Titles and Explanation	PR	Debit	Credit

Analysis component: _____

_____

_____

_____

_____

_____

Problem 7-5A

a.
_____

b.   **GENERAL JOURNAL**   Page____

Date	Account Titles and Explanation	PR	Debit	Credit

Analysis component: _____
_____
_____
_____
_____
_____

Name: _____

Problem 7-6A

a.

_____

_____

b.

GENERAL JOURNAL   Page____

Date	Account Titles and Explanation	PR	Debit	Credit

Name: _____

Problem 7-6A (concl'd.)

GENERAL JOURNAL

Page____

Date	Account Titles and Explanation	PR	Debit	Credit

Problem 7-7A

Part 1

Problem 7-7A (concl'd.)

Part 2

GENERAL JOURNAL

Page_____

Date	Account Titles and Explanation	PR	Debit	Credit

Analysis component: _____

_____

_____

_____

_____

_____

_____

_____

_____

_____

_____

_____

Problem 7-8A

Part 1

Part 2

GENERAL JOURNAL   Page_____

Date		Account Titles and Explanation	PR	Debit	Credit

Name: _____

Problem 7-8A (concl'd.)

Analysis component: _____

_____

_____

_____

_____

_____

_____

_____

_____

_____

_____

a. _____

_____

b.   **GENERAL JOURNAL**   Page____

Date		Account Titles and Explanation	PR	Debit	Credit

Problem 7-10A

a. _____
_____

b. **GENERAL JOURNAL** Page_____

Date		Account Titles and Explanation	PR	Debit	Credit

Name: _____

Problem 7-11A

Part 1

Part 2

GENERAL JOURNAL

Page_____

Date		Account Titles and Explanation	PR	Debit	Credit

Problem 7-11A (concl'd.)

GENERAL JOURNAL   Page_____

Date		Account Titles and Explanation	PR	Debit	Credit

Analysis component:

_____
_____
_____
_____
_____
_____
_____
_____

Problem 7-1B

(1) Principle Violated:	
Recommendation:	

(2) Principle Violated:	
Recommendation:	

(3) Principle Violated:	
Recommendation:	

(4) Principle Violated:	
Recommendation:	

(5) Principle Violated:	
Recommendation:	

Problem 7-2B

Part 1   **GENERAL JOURNAL**   Page_____

Date	Account Titles and Explanation	PR	Debit	Credit

Part 2

Baby Photography
Petty Cash Payments Report
July 5 – 31, 2020

Receipts:
_____
_____
_____
_____
_____
_____
_____
_____
_____
_____
_____
_____
_____

Fund total
Less: Cash remaining
Equals: Cash required to replenish petty cash
Cash over/(short)

Part 3   **GENERAL JOURNAL**   Page_____

Date	Account Titles and Explanation	PR	Debit	Credit

Name: _____

Problem 7-2B (concl'd.)

Analysis component: _____

_____
_____
_____
_____
_____
_____
_____

Problem 7-3B

GENERAL JOURNAL

Page_____

Date	Account Titles and Explanation	PR	Debit	Credit

Analysis component: _____

_____
_____
_____
_____
_____

Name: _____

Problem 7-4B

GENERAL JOURNAL   Page____

Date	Account Titles and Explanation	PR	Debit	Credit

Analysis component: _____

_____

_____

_____

_____

_____

_____

Problem 7-5B

a.

_____

_____

_____

b. <div align="center">**GENERAL JOURNAL**</div> Page_____

Date	Account Titles and Explanation	PR	Debit	Credit

Analysis component: _____

_____

_____

_____

_____

_____

_____

_____

Problem 7-6B

a.

_____

_____

_____

b.

GENERAL JOURNAL

Page_____

Date		Account Titles and Explanation	PR	Debit	Credit

Name: _____

Problem 7-7B

Part 1

Part 2

GENERAL JOURNAL

Page____

Date	Account Titles and Explanation	PR	Debit	Credit

Name: _____

Problem 7-7B (concl'd.)

Analysis component: _____

_____
_____
_____
_____
_____
_____
_____
_____

Problem 7-8B   Part 1

_____
_____

Part 2   **GENERAL JOURNAL**   Page____

Date	Account Titles and Explanation	PR	Debit	Credit

Name: _____

Problem 7-8B (concl'd.)

GENERAL JOURNAL

Page_____

Date	Account Titles and Explanation	PR	Debit	Credit

Analysis component: _____

_____

_____

_____

_____

_____

_____

_____

_____

_____

Problem 7-9B   Part 1

_____
_____
_____

Part 2 　　　　　　　　　　**GENERAL JOURNAL** 　　　　　　　　　　Page____

Date	Account Titles and Explanation	PR	Debit	Credit

Name: _____

Problem 7-10B   Part 1

_____
_____

Part 2   **GENERAL JOURNAL**   Page____

Date	Account Titles and Explanation	PR	Debit	Credit

Name: _____

Problem 7-11B   Part 1

Name: _____

Problem 7-11B (concl'd.)

Part 2

	GENERAL JOURNAL			Page____

Date	Account Titles and Explanation	PR	Debit	Credit

Analysis component: _____

_____

_____

_____

_____

_____

_____

Quick Study 8-1

GENERAL JOURNAL

Date	Account Titles and Explanation	PR	Debit	Credit

Quick Study 8-2

(a) _____

_____

_____

_____

_____

(b) _____

_____

_____

_____

_____

(c) _____

_____

_____

_____

_____

(d) _____

_____

_____

_____

_____

Quick Study 8-3

GENERAL JOURNAL

Date	Account Titles and Explanation	PR	Debit	Credit

Quick Study 8-4

Biotech		
Partial Balance Sheet		
December 31, 2020		

Quick Study 8-5

GENERAL JOURNAL

Date	Account Titles and Explanation	PR	Debit	Credit

Quick Study 8-6

a.

Allowance for Doubtful Accounts

b. _____

_____

_____

_____

_____

c.

GENERAL JOURNAL   Page____

Date		Account Titles and Explanation	PR	Debit	Credit

Quick Study 8-7

Allowance for Doubtful Accounts

GENERAL JOURNAL   Page____

Date		Account Titles and Explanation	PR	Debit	Credit

Quick Study 8-8

a.   GENERAL JOURNAL   Page_____

Date		Account Titles and Explanation	PR	Debit	Credit

b. _____

_____

c. _____

_____

Quick Study 8-9

GENERAL JOURNAL   Page_____

Date		Account Titles and Explanation	PR	Debit	Credit

Allowance for Doubtful Accounts

Quick Study 8-10

GENERAL JOURNAL   Page_____

Date		Account Titles and Explanation	PR	Debit	Credit

Quick Study 8-11

GENERAL JOURNAL   Page_____

Date		Account Titles and Explanation	PR	Debit	Credit

Quick Study 8-12

GENERAL JOURNAL

Date		Account Titles and Explanation	PR	Debit	Credit

Quick Study 8-13

GENERAL JOURNAL

Date		Account Titles and Explanation	PR	Debit	Credit

Quick Study 8-14

a. _____

b. _____

c. _____

*Quick Study 8-15

GENERAL JOURNAL

Date		Account Titles and Explanation	PR	Debit	Credit

*Quick Study 8-16

GENERAL JOURNAL

Date		Account Titles and Explanation	PR	Debit	Credit

Calculations:

_____

_____

_____

_____

_____

_____

_____

Part 1

GENERAL LEDGER

Accounts Receivable	Sales	Sales Returns and Allowances

ACCOUNTS RECEIVABLE SUBLEDGER

ABC Shop	Colt Enterprises	Red McKenzie

Part 2

Comparison:

Exercise 8-2

1. _____

_____

_____

_____

_____

2. _____

_____

_____

_____

_____

3. _____

_____

_____

_____

_____

4. _____

_____

_____

_____

_____

Name: _____

Exercise 8-3

1.

Weakness #1	
Implication	
Recommendation	
Weakness #2	
Implication	
Recommendation	

Name: _____

Exercise 8-3 (cont'd.)

Weakness #3	
Implication	
Recommendation	
Weakness #4	
Implication	
Recommendation	

2. _____

_____

_____

_____

_____

_____

_____

_____

_____

_____

Exercise 8-4

GENERAL JOURNAL

Date		Account Titles and Explanation	PR	Debit	Credit

Exercise 8-5

GENERAL JOURNAL

Date		Account Titles and Explanation	PR	Debit	Credit

Name: _____

Exercise 8-6

GENERAL JOURNAL

Date		Account Titles and Explanation	PR	Debit	Credit

Name: _____

Exercise 8-7

a.

Accounts Receivable	Allowance for Doubtful Accounts

GENERAL JOURNAL

Date	Account Titles and Explanation	PR	Debit	Credit

b.

Accounts Receivable	Allowance for Doubtful Accounts

GENERAL JOURNAL

Date	Account Titles and Explanation	PR	Debit	Credit

Exercise 8-8

1.

GENERAL JOURNAL

Date		Account Titles and Explanation	PR	Debit	Credit

2.

Accounts Receivable

Allowance for Doubtful Accounts

Bad debt expense

Exercise 8-9

a. _____

b. _____

c. _____

d. _____

e. _____

Exercise 8-10

Partial Balance Sheet		

Name: _____

Exercise 8-11

| a, b, and c | | **GENERAL JOURNAL** | | | Page____ |

Date		Account Titles and Explanation	PR	Debit	Credit

Calculations:

Accounts Receivable   **Allowance for Doubtful Accounts**

Exercise 8-11 (concl'd.)

d.

Partial Balance Sheet		

Analysis component:

_____

_____

_____

_____

_____

Exercise 8-12

a, b, and c.   **GENERAL JOURNAL**   Page____

Date	Account Titles and Explanation	PR	Debit	Credit

Date	Account Titles and Explanation	PR	Debit	Credit

Exercise 8-12 (concl'd.)

Calculations:

Accounts Receivable	Allowance for Doubtful Accounts

d.

Partial Balance Sheet		

Analysis component:

_____
_____
_____
_____
_____
_____

Exercise 8-13

a and b.   **GENERAL JOURNAL**   Page_____

Date	Account Titles and Explanation	PR	Debit	Credit

Calculations:

Accounts Receivable   **Allowance for Doubtful Accounts**

c.

Partial Balance Sheet

Analysis component:

_____

_____

_____

_____

_____

_____

Exercise 8-14

GENERAL JOURNAL

Page____

Date		Account Titles and Explanation	PR	Debit	Credit

Analysis component:

_____
_____
_____
_____
_____
_____
_____
_____
_____

Exercise 8-15

1. _____
_____
_____
_____

2. _____
_____

3. _____

GENERAL JOURNAL

Page____

Date		Account Titles and Explanation	PR	Debit	Credit

Exercise 8-16

GENERAL JOURNAL

Date		Account Titles and Explanation	PR	Debit	Credit

Exercise 8-17

GENERAL JOURNAL

Date		Account Titles and Explanation	PR	Debit	Credit

Exercise 8-18

GENERAL JOURNAL

Date		Account Titles and Explanation	PR	Debit	Credit

Name: _____

Exercise 8-19

Part 1

Accounts Receivable Turnover	Days' Sales Uncollected

Part 2

_____
_____
_____
_____
_____
_____
_____
_____
_____

Name: _____

*Exercise 8-20

GENERAL JOURNAL

Date	Account Titles and Explanation	PR	Debit	Credit

Financial Statement Note(s):

_____

_____

_____

_____

Fundamental Accounting Principles, 16ce, Working Papers

Name: _____

*Exercise 8-21

GENERAL JOURNAL

Date		Account Titles and Explanation	PR	Debit	Credit

Calculations:

_____

_____

_____

_____

_____

_____

_____
_____
_____
_____
_____
_____
_____
_____
_____
_____
_____
_____
_____
_____
_____
_____
_____
_____

Problem 8-2A

a. Expense is 2% of credit sales:

GENERAL JOURNAL

Date		Account Titles and Explanation	PR	Debit	Credit

b. Allowance is 5% of accounts receivable:

GENERAL JOURNAL

Date		Account Titles and Explanation	PR	Debit	Credit

Calculations for Part b:

**Allowance for
Doubtful Accounts**

Problem 8-2A (cont'd.)

Part 2

Part 3

Analysis component:

_____

_____

_____

_____

_____

Problem 8-3A   Part 1

Calculation of the required balance of the allowance (using an aging analysis):

Not due:	
1 to 30:	
31 to 60:	
61 to 90:	
Over 90:	

Allowance for Doubtful Accounts

Part 2

GENERAL JOURNAL

Date	Account Titles and Explanation	PR	Debit	Credit

Analysis component:

_____

_____

_____

_____

_____

_____

Name: _____

Problem 8-4A Part 1

Calculation of the required balance of the allowance (using an aging analysis):

Not due:	
1 to 30:	
31 to 60:	
61 to 90:	
Over 90:	

___Allowance for Doubtful Accounts___

Part 2

GENERAL JOURNAL

Date	Account Titles and Explanation	PR	Debit	Credit

Analysis component:

_____

_____

_____

_____

_____

Name: _____

Problem 8-5A   Part A

Part 1   **GENERAL JOURNAL**   Page_____

Date	Account Titles and Explanation	PR	Debit	Credit

Name: _____

Problem 8-5A (concl'd.)

Part B

Part 2   GENERAL JOURNAL   Page____

Date	Account Titles and Explanation	PR	Debit	Credit

Part 3

Part 4

_____

_____

Part C

Part 5   GENERAL JOURNAL   Page____

Date	Account Titles and Explanation	PR	Debit	Credit

Calculations:

Accounts Receivable	Allowance for Doubtful Accounts

Part 6

Part 7

_____

_____

Name: _____

Problem 8-6A

GENERAL JOURNAL

Date	Account Titles and Explanation	PR	Debit	Credit
2020				
a.				
b.				
c.				
d.				

Calculations:

Accounts Receivable	Allowance for Doubtful Accounts

Fundamental Accounting Principles, 16ce, Working Papers

Name: _____

Problem 8-6A (concl'd.)

GENERAL JOURNAL

Date	Account Titles and Explanation	PR	Debit	Credit
2021				
e.				
f.				
g.				
h.				

Calculations:

Accounts Receivable	Allowance for Doubtful Accounts

Problem 8-7A

Part 1

a.

GENERAL JOURNAL

Date	Account Titles and Explanation	PR	Debit	Credit
2020				

Allowance for Doubtful Accounts

b.

Part2

c.

GENERAL JOURNAL

Date	Account Titles and Explanation	PR	Debit	Credit
2020				

Calculations:

Allowance for Doubtful Accounts

d.

Problem 8-8A

Part 1

GENERAL JOURNAL

Date		Account Titles and Explanation	PR	Debit	Credit

Part 2

GENERAL JOURNAL

Date	Account Titles and Explanation	PR	Debit	Credit

Calculations:

Accounts Receivable	**Allowance for Doubtful Accounts**

Problem 8-9A

a.

Customer	Not yet due 0.5%	1 to 29 days past due 1%	30 to 59 days past due 4%	60 to 89 days past due 10%	90 to 119 days past due 20%	Over 119 days past due 50%
B. Axley						
T. Holton						
W. Nix						
C. Percy						
K. Willis						

Month

b.   **GENERAL JOURNAL**   Page____

Date	Account Titles and Explanation	PR	Debit	Credit

Calculations:

Accounts Receivable	Allowance for Doubtful Accounts

Name: _____

Problem 8-10A

a. **GENERAL JOURNAL** Page_____

Date	Account Titles and Explanation	PR	Debit	Credit
2020				
2021				
2022				

Calculations:

Accounts Receivable   **Allowance for Doubtful Accounts**

Analysis component:

_____
_____
_____
_____
_____

Problem 8-11A

Parts a, b, and c.

Date of Note	Principal	Interest Rate	Term	Maturity Date	Days of Accrued Interest at Dec. 31, 2020	Accrued Interest at Dec. 31, 2020
Nov. 1/19	$240,000	4%	180 days			
Jan. 5/20	$100,000	5%	90 days			
Nov. 20/20	$90,000	4.5%	45 days			
Dec. 10/20	$120,000	5.5%	30 days			

Calculations:

_____
_____
_____
_____
_____
_____
_____
_____
_____
_____
_____
_____
_____
_____
_____

d.   **GENERAL JOURNAL**   Page____

Date		Account Titles and Explanation	PR	Debit	Credit

e.   **GENERAL JOURNAL**   Page____

Date		Account Titles and Explanation	PR	Debit	Credit

Name: _____

Problem 8-12A

Parts a, b, and c.

Date of Note	Principal	Interest Rate	Term	Maturity Date	Days of Accrued Interest at Jul. 31, 2020	Accrued Interest at Jul. 31, 2020
Dec. 1/19	$170,000	4%	180 days			
April 5/20	$71,000	5%	90 days			
June 20/20	$64,000	4.5%	45 days			
July 10/20	$85,000	5.5%	30 days			

Calculations:

_____
_____
_____
_____
_____
_____
_____
_____
_____
_____
_____
_____
_____

d. GENERAL JOURNAL Page____

Date	Account Titles and Explanation	PR	Debit	Credit

e. GENERAL JOURNAL Page____

Date	Account Titles and Explanation	PR	Debit	Credit

Name: _____

Problem 8-13A

a.

GENERAL JOURNAL

Page_____

Date	Account Titles and Explanation	PR	Debit	Credit

Fundamental Accounting Principles, 16ce, Working Papers

Problem 8-13A (concl'd.)

b. Determine the maturity date of the note dated March 2:

_____

_____

_____

_____

_____

Prepare the entry on the maturity date:

GENERAL JOURNAL   Page____

Date	Account Titles and Explanation	PR	Debit	Credit

GENERAL JOURNAL

Name: _____

Page_____

Date	Account Titles and Explanation	PR	Debit	Credit

Analysis component:

_____

_____

_____

_____

_____

Name: _____

Problem 8-15A

	2018	**2017**
a. Accounts receivable turnover ratio		
b. Days' sales uncollected		

Comments: _____
_____
_____
_____
_____
_____

*Problem 8-16A

GENERAL JOURNAL   Page_____

Date		Account Titles and Explanation	PR	Debit	Credit

Name: _____

*Problem 8-16A (cont'd.)

GENERAL JOURNAL

Page____

Date		Account Titles and Explanation	PR	Debit	Credit

Analysis component: _____

_____
_____
_____
_____
_____

*Problem 8-17A

GENERAL JOURNAL

Page____

Date		Account Titles and Explanation	PR	Debit	Credit

*Problem 8-17A (cont'd.)

GENERAL JOURNAL

Page____

Date	Account Titles and Explanation	PR	Debit	Credit

*Problem 8-17A (cont'd.)

GENERAL JOURNAL

Date	Account Titles and Explanation	PR	Debit	Credit

Problem 8-1B

_____
_____
_____
_____
_____
_____
_____
_____
_____
_____
_____
_____
_____
_____

Problem 8-2B

a. Expense is 3% of credit sales:

GENERAL JOURNAL

Date		Account Titles and Explanation	PR	Debit	Credit

b. Allowance is 6% of accounts receivable:

GENERAL JOURNAL

Date		Account Titles and Explanation	PR	Debit	Credit

Calculations for Part b:

Allowance for Doubtful Accounts

Problem 8-2B (concl'd.)

Part 2

Part 3

Analysis component:

_____

_____

_____

_____

_____

Problem 8-3B   Part 1

Calculation of the required balance of the allowance (using an aging analysis):

Not due:	
1 to 30:	
31 to 60:	
61 to 90:	
Over 90:	

Allowance for Doubtful Accounts

Part 2

GENERAL JOURNAL

Date	Account Titles and Explanation	PR	Debit	Credit

Analysis component:

_____

_____

_____

_____

_____

_____

Problem 8-4B   Part 1

Calculation of the required balance of the allowance (using an aging analysis):

Not due:	
1 to 30:	
31 to 60:	
61 to 90:	
Over 90:	

Allowance for Doubtful Accounts

Part 2

GENERAL JOURNAL

Date	Account Titles and Explanation	PR	Debit	Credit

Analysis component:

_____
_____
_____
_____
_____
_____

Name: _____

Problem 8-5B   Part A

Part 1   GENERAL JOURNAL   Page_____

Date		Account Titles and Explanation	PR	Debit	Credit

Problem 8-5B (concl'd.)

Part B

Part 2   GENERAL JOURNAL   Page_____

Date		Account Titles and Explanation	PR	Debit	Credit

Part 3

Part 4

_____

_____

Part C

Part 5   GENERAL JOURNAL   Page_____

Date		Account Titles and Explanation	PR	Debit	Credit

Calculations:

Accounts Receivable	Allowance for Doubtful Accounts

Part 6

Part 7

_____

_____

Name: _____

Problem 8-6B

GENERAL JOURNAL

Date	Account Titles and Explanation	PR	Debit	Credit
2020				
a.				
b.				
c.				
d.				

Calculations:

Accounts Receivable   **Allowance for Doubtful Accounts**

Problem 8-6B (concl'd.)

GENERAL JOURNAL

Date	Account Titles and Explanation	PR	Debit	Credit
2021				
e.				
f.				
g.				
h.				

Calculations:

Accounts Receivable	Allowance for Doubtful Accounts

Name: _____

Problem 8-7B

Part 1

Part a

GENERAL JOURNAL

Date	Account Titles and Explanation	PR	Debit	Credit
2020				

Allowance for Doubtful Accounts

Part b

Part 2

Part c

GENERAL JOURNAL

Date	Account Titles and Explanation	PR	Debit	Credit
2020				

Calculations:

Allowance for Doubtful Accounts

Part d

Problem 8-8B

Part 1

GENERAL JOURNAL

Date	Account Titles and Explanation	PR	Debit	Credit

Part 2

GENERAL JOURNAL

Date	Account Titles and Explanation	PR	Debit	Credit

Calculations:

Accounts Receivable	Allowance for Doubtful Accounts

Name: _____

Problem 8-9B

a.

Month

Customer	Not yet due 1.5%	1 to 29 days past due 2%	30 to 59 days past due 5%	60 to 89 days past due 20%	90 to 119 days past due 35%	Over 119 days past due 50%
A. Leslie						
T. Meston						
P. Obrian						
L. Timms						
W. Victor						

b.   **GENERAL JOURNAL**   Page____

Date		Account Titles and Explanation	PR	Debit	Credit

Calculations:

Accounts Receivable   **Allowance for Doubtful Accounts**

Name: _____

Problem 8-10B

a.   **GENERAL JOURNAL**   Page_____

Date	Account Titles and Explanation	PR	Debit	Credit
2020				
2021				
2022				

Calculations:

Accounts Receivable	Allowance for Doubtful Accounts

Analysis component:

_____

_____

_____

_____

_____

Chapter 8

Name: _____

Problem 8-11B

Parts a, b, and c.

Date of Note	Principal	Interest Rate	Term	Maturity Date	Days of Accrued Interest at Dec. 31, 2020	Accrued Interest at Dec. 31, 2020
Sept. 20/19	$490,000	3%	120 days			
June 01/20	$240,000	3.5%	45 days			
Nov. 23/20	$164,000	4.5%	90 days			
Dec. 18/20	$120,000	4%	30 days			

Calculations:

_____
_____
_____
_____
_____
_____
_____
_____
_____
_____
_____
_____
_____

d.   **GENERAL JOURNAL**   Page_____

Date	Account Titles and Explanation	PR	Debit	Credit

e.   **GENERAL JOURNAL**   Page_____

Date	Account Titles and Explanation	PR	Debit	Credit

Name: _____

Problem 8-12B

Parts a, b, and c.

Date of Note	Principal	Interest Rate	Term	Maturity Date	Days of Accrued Interest at Dec. 31, 2020	Accrued Interest at Dec. 31, 2020
Nov. 01/19	$370,000	3%	180 days			
Jan. 05/20	$212,000	3.5%	120 days			
Nov. 20/20	$102,000	4.5%	90 days			
Dec. 10/20	$135,000	5.5%	30 days			

Calculations:

_____
_____
_____
_____
_____
_____
_____
_____
_____
_____
_____
_____

d. **GENERAL JOURNAL** Page____

Date	Account Titles and Explanation	PR	Debit	Credit

e. **GENERAL JOURNAL** Page____

Date	Account Titles and Explanation	PR	Debit	Credit

Problem 8-13B

a.   **GENERAL JOURNAL**   **Page____**

Date		Account Titles and Explanation	PR	Debit	Credit

Problem 8-13B (concl'd.)

b. Determine the maturity date of the note dated March 1:

_____

_____

_____

_____

_____

_____

Prepare the entry on the maturity date:

GENERAL JOURNAL   Page____

Date	Account Titles and Explanation	PR	Debit	Credit

Name: _____

Problem 8-14B

Parts (a) to (f)

GENERAL JOURNAL   Page____

Date	Account Titles and Explanation	PR	Debit	Credit

Analysis component: _____

_____

_____

_____

_____

Problem 8-15B

	2017	2016
c. Accounts receivable turnover ratio		
d. Days' sales uncollected		

Comments: _____
_____
_____
_____
_____
_____
_____

*Problem 8-16B

GENERAL JOURNAL   Page_____

Date	Account Titles and Explanation	PR	Debit	Credit

*Problem 8-16B (cont'd.)

GENERAL JOURNAL   Page____

Date		Account Titles and Explanation	PR	Debit	Credit

Analysis component: _____

_____

_____

_____

_____

*Problem 8-17B

GENERAL JOURNAL   Page____

Date		Account Titles and Explanation	PR	Debit	Credit

Name: _____

*Problem 8-17B (cont'd.)

GENERAL JOURNAL   Page____

Date	Account Titles and Explanation	PR	Debit	Credit

Name: _____

*Problem 8-17B (concl'd.)

GENERAL JOURNAL   Page_____

Date	Account Titles and Explanation	PR	Debit	Credit

Quick Study 9-1

_____
_____
_____

Quick Study 9-2

_____
_____
_____
_____
_____
_____
_____

Quick Study 9-3

(1)
(a) _____   **(c)** _____
(b) _____   **(d)** _____

(2)

GENERAL JOURNAL   Page____

Date		Account Titles and Explanation	PR	Debit	Credit

Name: _____

Quick Study 9-4

PPE Item	(a) Appraised Values	(b) Ratio of Individual Appraised Value to Total Appraised Value (a) ÷ Total Appraised Value	(c) Cost Allocation (b) × Total Actual Cost
Land			
Building			
Totals			

GENERAL JOURNAL

Page____

Date	Account Titles and Explanation	PR	Debit	Credit

Name: _____

Quick Study 9-5

Quick Study 9-6

_____

_____

_____

Quick Study 9-7

_____

Year	Calculation	Annual Depreciation
2020		
2021		
2022		
2023		
2024		
Total		

Name: _____

Quick Study 9-8

_____

_____

Year	Calculation	Annual Depreciation
2020		
2021		
2022		
2023		
2024		
Total		

Quick Study 9-9

_____

_____

_____

_____

_____

_____

_____

_____

_____

_____

_____

_____

_____

_____

_____

_____

_____

_____

_____

_____

_____

Quick Study 9-10

a. _____

_____

_____

b. _____

_____

_____

_____

Name: _____

Quick Study 9-11

a. _____
_____
_____

b. _____
_____
_____
_____

Quick Study 9-12

a. _____
_____
_____

b. _____
_____
_____

Quick Study 9-13

_____
_____
_____
_____
_____
_____
_____
_____
_____

Quick Study 9-14

	GENERAL JOURNAL			Page_____

Date	Account Titles and Explanation	PR	Debit	Credit

Calculations:
_____
_____
_____
_____
_____
_____
_____
_____
_____

Quick Study 9-15
_____
_____
_____
_____
_____

Calculations:

Asset	Cost	Accumulated Depreciation	Book Value	Recoverable Amount	Impairment Loss
Building	$1,200,000	$465,000		$735,000	
Computer	3,500	1,800		200	
Furniture	79,000	53,000		5,000	
Land	630,000	0		790,000	
Machine	284,000	117,000		172,000	

Name: _____

Quick Study 9-16

a.

GENERAL JOURNAL

Page____

Date		Account Titles and Explanation	PR	Debit	Credit

b.

GENERAL JOURNAL

Page____

Date		Account Titles and Explanation	PR	Debit	Credit

c.

GENERAL JOURNAL

Page____

Date		Account Titles and Explanation	PR	Debit	Credit

d.

GENERAL JOURNAL

Page____

Date		Account Titles and Explanation	PR	Debit	Credit

Fundamental Accounting Principles, 16ce, Working Papers

Name: _____

Quick Study 9-17

GENERAL JOURNAL

Page_____

Date		Account Titles and Explanation	PR	Debit	Credit

Calculations: _____

_____

_____

_____

_____

Quick Study 9-18

GENERAL JOURNAL

Page_____

Date		Account Titles and Explanation	PR	Debit	Credit

Calculations: _____

_____

_____

_____

_____

Name: _____

Quick Study 9-19

GENERAL JOURNAL

Page____

Date		Account Titles and Explanation	PR	Debit	Credit

Quick Study 9-20

GENERAL JOURNAL

Page____

Date		Account Titles and Explanation	PR	Debit	Credit

Calculations: _____
_____
_____
_____
_____
_____
_____

Name: _____

*Quick Study 9-21

	Calculation	
Motor (old)		
Motor (new)		
Metal housing		
Misc. parts		
Total depreciation expense to be recorded on the machine for 2020 =		

Exercise 9-1

_____
_____
_____
_____
_____
_____
_____
_____
_____
_____

Chapter 9   Name:_____

Exercise 9-2

Cost of land:

_____
_____
_____
_____
_____
_____
_____

Cost of building:

_____
_____
_____
_____
_____
_____
_____

Journal entry:

GENERAL JOURNAL   Page_____

Date	Account Titles and Explanation	PR	Debit	Credit

Name: _____

Exercise 9-3

PPE Asset	(a) Appraised Values	(b) Ratio of Individual Appraised Value to Total Appraised Value (a) ÷ Total Appraised Value	(c) Cost Allocation (b) × Total Actual Cost
Land			
Land Imp.			
Building			
Totals			

Journal entry:

GENERAL JOURNAL   Page____

Date		Account Titles and Explanation	PR	Debit	Credit

Exercise 9-4

GENERAL JOURNAL

Date	Account Titles and Explanation	PR	Debit	Credit

Calculations:

PPE Asset	(a) Appraised Values	(b) Ratio of Individual Appraised Value to Total Appraised Value *(a) ÷ Total Appraised Value*	(c) Cost Allocation *(b) × Total Actual Cost*
Land			
Building			
Equip.			
Tools			
Totals			

Name: _____

Exercise 9-5

GENERAL JOURNAL   Page____

Date	Account Titles and Explanation	PR	Debit	Credit

Calculations:

_____
_____
_____
_____
_____
_____
_____

Chapter 9

Name: _____

Exercise 9-6

Year	Straight-Line
2018	
2019	
2020	
2021	
TOTAL	

Year	Double-Declining-Balance
2018	
2019	
2020	
2021	
TOTAL	

Year	Units-of-Production
2018	
2019	
2020	
2021	
TOTAL	

Fundamental Accounting Principles, 16ce, Working Papers

Name: _____

Exercise 9-7

a. _____

b. _____

c. _____

Analysis component:

_____
_____
_____
_____
_____
_____
_____
_____

Name: _____

Exercise 9-8

Year	Straight-Line Method	
	Depreciation Expense	**Book Value at December 31**
2020		
2021		
2022		
2023		
2024		

Year	Double-Declining Balance Method	
	Depreciation Expense	**Book Value at December 31**
2020		
2021		
2022		
2023		
2024		

Year	Units-of-Production Method	
	Depreciation Expense	**Book Value at December 31**
2020		
2021		
2022		
2023		
2024		

Analysis component: _____

a. _____

b. _____
_____

Fundamental Accounting Principles, 16ce, Working Papers

Exercise 9-9

Step 1: Cost allocation

PPE Asset	(a) Appraised Values	(b) Ratio of Individual Appraised Value to Total Appraised Value *(a) ÷ Total Appraised Value*	(c) Cost Allocation *(b) × Total Actual Cost*
Land			
Building			
Equip.			
Tools			
Totals			

Step 2: Calculate depreciation

PPE asset	Cost (from c above)	2020 Depreciation	2021 Depreciation
Land			
Building			
Equip.			
Tools			

Analysis component: _____

_____

_____

_____

_____

_____

Exercise 9-10

Description	Date of Purchase	Depreciation Method	Cost Information				Balance of Accum. Deprec. Dec. 31, 2019	Depreciation		
			Cost	Residual Value	Life			Depreciation Expense for 2020	Balance of Accum. Deprec. Dec. 31, 2020
Building	May 2, 2014	S/L	$650,000	$250,000	10 yr.	$226,667			
Modular Furniture	May 2, 2014	S/L	72,000	0	6 yr.	68,000			
Truck	January 25, 2017	DDB	80,000	10,000	8 yr.	45,313			

Analysis component:

_____

_____

_____

_____

Fundamental Accounting Principles, 16ce, Working Papers

Exercise 9-11

	Dynamic Exploration			
	Partial Balance Sheet			
	December 31, 2019			

Exercise 9-12

a. Straight-line

	Year 1	Year 2	Year 3	Year 4	Year 5	5-Year Totals
Profit before deprec.						
Deprec. expense						
Profit						

b. Double-declining-balance

	Year 1	Year 2	Year 3	Year 4	Year 5	5-Year Totals
Profit before deprec.						
Deprec. expense						
Profit (loss)						

Analysis component: _____
_____
_____
_____
_____
_____

Fundamental Accounting Principles, 16ce, Working Papers

735

Name: _____

Exercise 9-13

| Year | Depreciation | |
	Straight-Line	Units-of-Production
2018		
2019		
2020		

Analysis component: _____
_____
_____
_____

Exercise 9-14

| Year | Depreciation | |
	Straight-Line	Double-Declining-Balance
2019		
2020		
2021		

Analysis component: _____
_____
_____
_____

Exercise 9-15

Year	(a) Straight-line	(b) Double-declining balance
2020		
2021		

Exercise 9-16

1. _____
_____

2. _____
_____
_____

Exercise 9-17

GENERAL JOURNAL   Page_____

Date	Account Titles and Explanation	PR	Debit	Credit

Calculations:

Name: _____

Exercise 9-18

Part 1   GENERAL JOURNAL   Page____

Date	Account Titles and Explanation	PR	Debit	Credit

Part 2   GENERAL JOURNAL   Page____

Date	Account Titles and Explanation	PR	Debit	Credit

Exercise 9-19

Part 1   GENERAL JOURNAL   Page____

Date	Account Titles and Explanation	PR	Debit	Credit

Part 2   GENERAL JOURNAL   Page____

Date	Account Titles and Explanation	PR	Debit	Credit

Name: _____

Exercise 9-19 (concluded)

GENERAL JOURNAL   Page_____

Date		Account Titles and Explanation	PR	Debit	Credit

Calculations:

Asset	Cost	Accum. Deprec.	Book Value	Recoverable Amount	Impairment Loss	2021 Dep. Exp.
Equipment	$40,000	$20,000		$ 8,000		
Furniture	12,000	9,509		2,950		
Land	85,000	N/A		101,800		
Office Bldng	77,000	23,000		52,500		
Warehouse	55,000	12,938		45,100		

Name: _____

Exercise 9-20

a.

		GENERAL JOURNAL			Page_____
Date		Account Titles and Explanation	PR	Debit	Credit

b.

		GENERAL JOURNAL			Page_____
Date		Account Titles and Explanation	PR	Debit	Credit

c.

		GENERAL JOURNAL			Page_____
Date		Account Titles and Explanation	PR	Debit	Credit

d.

		GENERAL JOURNAL			Page_____
Date		Account Titles and Explanation	PR	Debit	Credit

Chapter 9   Name: _____

Exercise 9-21

To record partial year's depreciation in 2021:

GENERAL JOURNAL   Page____

Date	Account Titles and Explanation	PR	Debit	Credit

a.   GENERAL JOURNAL   Page____

Date	Account Titles and Explanation	PR	Debit	Credit

b.   GENERAL JOURNAL   Page____

Date	Account Titles and Explanation	PR	Debit	Credit

a. _____

_____

b. _____

_____

_____

_____

_____

c. _____

_____

d. **GENERAL JOURNAL**   Page_____

Date		Account Titles and Explanation	PR	Debit	Credit

Name: _____

Exercise 9-23

GENERAL JOURNAL

Page_____

Date		Account Titles and Explanation	PR	Debit	Credit
a.					
b.					

Analysis component: _____

_____

_____

_____

_____

_____

Exercise 9-24

GENERAL JOURNAL   Page____

Date	Account Titles and Explanation	PR	Debit	Credit
a.				
b.				
c.				
d.				

Exercise 9-25

GENERAL JOURNAL   Page____

Date	Account Titles and Explanation	PR	Debit	Credit

Name: _____

GENERAL JOURNAL

Page____

Date	Account Titles and Explanation	PR	Debit	Credit
Part 1.				
Part 2.				

_____

_____

| | GENERAL JOURNAL | | | Page_____ |

Date	Account Titles and Explanation	PR	Debit	Credit

Fundamental Accounting Principles, 16ce, Working Papers

Name: _____

*Exercise 9-30

Part 1   **GENERAL JOURNAL**   Page_____

Date		Account Titles and Explanation	PR	Debit	Credit

Part 2: _____

_____

_____

_____

_____

_____

_____

_____

_____

_____

_____

_____

_____

_____

_____

Part 3: _____

_____

_____

_____

_____

_____

_____

Name: _____

Problem 9-1A

Part 1

	Land	Building 2	Building 3	Land Improv. 1	Land Improv. 2
Purchase price..........					
Demolition.................					
Landscaping..............					
New building............					
New improvements..					
Totals					

Calculations:

	Appraised Value	*Percent of Total*	*Apportioned Cost*
Land			
Building 2.................................			
Land Improvements 1			
Totals			

Part 2

GENERAL JOURNAL   Page_____

Date	Account Titles and Explanation	PR	Debit	Credit

Problem 9-2A

<table>
<tr><td colspan="5" align="center">Derlak Enterprises</td></tr>
<tr><td colspan="5" align="center">Balance Sheet</td></tr>
<tr><td colspan="5" align="center">December 31</td></tr>
<tr><td></td><td colspan="2" align="center">**2020**</td><td colspan="2" align="center">**2019**</td></tr>
<tr><td></td><td></td><td></td><td></td><td></td></tr>
<tr><td></td><td></td><td></td><td></td><td></td></tr>
<tr><td></td><td></td><td></td><td></td><td></td></tr>
<tr><td></td><td></td><td></td><td></td><td></td></tr>
<tr><td></td><td></td><td></td><td></td><td></td></tr>
<tr><td></td><td></td><td></td><td></td><td></td></tr>
<tr><td></td><td></td><td></td><td></td><td></td></tr>
<tr><td></td><td></td><td></td><td></td><td></td></tr>
<tr><td></td><td></td><td></td><td></td><td></td></tr>
<tr><td></td><td></td><td></td><td></td><td></td></tr>
<tr><td></td><td></td><td></td><td></td><td></td></tr>
<tr><td></td><td></td><td></td><td></td><td></td></tr>
<tr><td></td><td></td><td></td><td></td><td></td></tr>
<tr><td></td><td></td><td></td><td></td><td></td></tr>
<tr><td></td><td></td><td></td><td></td><td></td></tr>
<tr><td></td><td></td><td></td><td></td><td></td></tr>
<tr><td></td><td></td><td></td><td></td><td></td></tr>
<tr><td></td><td></td><td></td><td></td><td></td></tr>
<tr><td></td><td></td><td></td><td></td><td></td></tr>
<tr><td></td><td></td><td></td><td></td><td></td></tr>
<tr><td></td><td></td><td></td><td></td><td></td></tr>
<tr><td></td><td></td><td></td><td></td><td></td></tr>
<tr><td></td><td></td><td></td><td></td><td></td></tr>
<tr><td></td><td></td><td></td><td></td><td></td></tr>
<tr><td></td><td></td><td></td><td></td><td></td></tr>
<tr><td></td><td></td><td></td><td></td><td></td></tr>
<tr><td></td><td></td><td></td><td></td><td></td></tr>
<tr><td></td><td></td><td></td><td></td><td></td></tr>
</table>

Problem 9-2A (concluded)

Analysis component:

_____

_____

_____

_____

_____

_____

_____

Problem 9-3A

Part a.

Year	Straight-Line
2018	
2019	
2020	
2021	
TOTAL	

Part b.

Year	Double-Declining-Balance
2018	
2019	
2020	
2021	
TOTAL	

Problem 9-3A (concl'd.)

Part c.

Year	Units-of-Production
2018	
2019	
2020	
2021	
TOTAL	

Part d.

_____

_____

_____

_____

_____

Name: _____

Problem 9-4A

Part 1 Purchased January 1, 2020

	2020	2021	2022
A. Double-declining-balance method			
Equipment	$415,000	$415,000	$415,000
Less: Accumulated depreciation................			
Year-end book value..................................			
Depreciation expense for the year			
B. Straight-line method			
Equipment	$415,000	$415,000	$415,000
Less: Accumulated depreciation................			
Year-end book value.................................			
Depreciation expense for the year			

Calculations: _____

_____

_____

_____

_____

_____

_____

Fundamental Accounting Principles, 16ce, Working Papers

Name: _____

Problem 9-4A (concluded)

Part 2 Purchased July 1, 2020

	2020	2021	2022
A. Double-declining-balance method			
Equipment...	**$415,000**	**$415,000**	**$415,000**
Less: Accumulated depreciation...............			
Year-end book value....................................			
Depreciation expense for the year..................			
B. Straight-line method			
Equipment	**$415,000**	**$415,000**	**$415,000**
Less: Accumulated depreciation...............			
Year-end book value....................................			
Depreciation expense for the year..................			

Calculations: _____
_____
_____
_____
_____
_____
_____

Name: _____

Problem 9-5A

| Year | Depreciation Method | | |
	Straight-Line	Double-Declining-Balance	Units-of-Production
2020			
2021			
2022			

Analysis component: _____
_____
_____
_____
_____
_____
_____
_____
_____

Name: _____

Problem 9-6A

Year	Depreciation Method:		
	Straight-line	**Double-declining balance**	**Units-of-production**
2020			
2021			
2022			

Calculations:

1. Double-declining-balance method

	<u>2020</u>	<u>2021</u>	<u>2022</u>
Equipment...			
Less: Accumulated depreciation..........			
Year-end book value...............................			
Depreciation expense for the year			

2. Straight-line method

	<u>2020</u>	<u>2021</u>	<u>2022</u>
Equipment...			
Less: Accumulated depreciation..........			
Year-end book value			
Depreciation expense for the year			

Problem 9-7A

Part 1

| | | GENERAL JOURNAL | | | Page_____ |

GENERAL JOURNAL

Date	Account Titles and Explanation	PR	Debit	Credit

Part 2

Big Sky Farms
Partial Balance Sheet
April 30, 2021

Name: _____

Problem 9-8A

Part 1

	Market Value	Percentage of Total	Apportioned Cost
Building			
Land			
Land improvements..............			
Vehicles................................			
Total.....................................			

GENERAL JOURNAL

Page____

Date	Account Titles and Explanation	PR	Debit	Credit

Part 2: 2020 straight-line depreciation on building:

_____

_____

_____

Part 3: 2020 double-declining-balance depreciation on land improvements:

_____

_____

_____

Analysis component:

_____

_____

_____

_____

_____

_____

_____

Name: _____

Problem 9-9A

Year	Depreciation		
	Straight-Line	**Units-of-Production**	**Double-Declining-Balance**
2020			
2021			
2022			
2023			
2024			
Totals			

Calculations:

Problem 9-10A

	Cost Information						Depreciation		
Description	Date of Purchase	Depreciation Method	Cost	Residual	Life	Balance of Accum. Deprec. Dec. 31, 2020	Balance of Accum. Deprec. Dec. 31, 2020	Depreciation Expense for 2021	Balance of Accum. Deprec. Dec. 31, 2021
Office equipment	March 27/17	Straight-line	$52,000	$14,000	10 yr.				
Machinery	June 4/17	Double-declining-balance	275,000	46,000	6 yr.				
Truck	Nov. 13/20	Units-of-production	113,000	26,000	250,000 km.				

Calculations:

Name: _____

Problem 9-11A

GENERAL JOURNAL

Page_____

Date	Account Titles and Explanation	PR	Debit	Credit

Calculations:

Name: _____

Problem 9-12A

GENERAL JOURNAL

Page_____

Date		Account Titles and Explanation	PR	Debit	Credit

Calculations:

Name: _____

Problem 9-13A

Part 1: Entry to record the purchase of the replacement blade:

GENERAL JOURNAL   Page_____

Date	Account Titles and Explanation	PR	Debit	Credit

Calculations:

Part 2: Total depreciation expense to be recorded on Machine #5027 for 2020:_____

Calculations:

Part 1   GENERAL JOURNAL   Page____

Date	Account Titles and Explanation	PR	Debit	Credit

Calculations:

Name: _____

Problem 9-14A (continued)

Part 2

Problem 9-14A (concl'd.)

Analysis component:

_____
_____
_____
_____
_____
_____
_____
_____
_____
_____

Problem 9-15A

Part 1   GENERAL JOURNAL   Page____

Date	Account Titles and Explanation	PR	Debit	Credit

Calculations:

Problem 9-15A (concl'd.)

Part 2   **GENERAL JOURNAL**   Page_____

Date	Account Titles and Explanation	PR	Debit	Credit

Calculations:

Name: _____

Problem 9-16A

Part 1   **GENERAL JOURNAL**   Page____

Date	Account Titles and Explanation	PR	Debit	Credit

Part 2   **GENERAL JOURNAL**   Page____

Date	Account Titles and Explanation	PR	Debit	Credit

Problem 9-16A (concl'd.)

Part 3(a)　　　　　　　　　　GENERAL JOURNAL　　　　　　　　　Page_____

Date		Account Titles and Explanation	PR	Debit	Credit

Part 3(b)　　　　　　　　　　GENERAL JOURNAL　　　　　　　　　Page_____

Date		Account Titles and Explanation	PR	Debit	Credit

Part 3(c)　　　　　　　　　　GENERAL JOURNAL　　　　　　　　　Page_____

Date		Account Titles and Explanation	PR	Debit	Credit

Calculations:

Name: _____

Problem 9-17A

GENERAL JOURNAL   Page____

Date	Account Titles and Explanation	PR	Debit	Credit

Calculations:

Name: _____

Problem 9-18A

a. Depreciation expense on first December 31 of each machine's life:

GENERAL JOURNAL

Page_____

Date		Account Titles and Explanation	PR	Debit	Credit

b. Purchase/exchange/disposal of each machine:

GENERAL JOURNAL

Page_____

Date		Account Titles and Explanation	PR	Debit	Credit

GENERAL JOURNAL

Date	Account Titles and Explanation	PR	Debit	Credit

Calculations:

Problem 9-19A

a.   GENERAL JOURNAL   Page____

Date		Account Titles and Explanation	PR	Debit	Credit

b.   GENERAL JOURNAL   Page____

Date		Account Titles and Explanation	PR	Debit	Credit

Problem 9-20A

Part 1   GENERAL JOURNAL   Page____

Date		Account Titles and Explanation	PR	Debit	Credit

Problem 9-20A (concl'd.)

Part 2   **GENERAL JOURNAL**   Page____

Date	Account Titles and Explanation	PR	Debit	Credit

*Problem 9-21A

1a.   GENERAL JOURNAL   Page____

Date	Account Titles and Explanation	PR	Debit	Credit

1b.   GENERAL JOURNAL   Page____

Date	Account Titles and Explanation	PR	Debit	Credit

Calculations:

Part 2

_____
_____
_____
_____
_____
_____

Name: _____

Problem 9-1B

Part 1

	Land	Building B	Building C	Land Improv. B	Land Improv. C
Purchase price............					
Demolition..................					
Landscaping................					
New building..............					
New improvements....					
Totals					

Calculations:

Allocation of purchase price:

	Appraised Value	*Percent of Total*	*Apportioned Cost*
Land	$317,034		
Building B......................................	189,108		
Land Improvements B	50,058		
Totals	$556,200	100 %	$540,000

Part 2

GENERAL JOURNAL

Page_____

Date	Account Titles and Explanation	PR	Debit	Credit

Name: _____

Problem 9-2B

	Xentel Interactive Balance Sheet September 30			
	2020		**2019**	

Fundamental Accounting Principles, 16ce, Working Papers

Name: _____

Problem 9-2B (concl'd.)

Analysis component:

_____
_____
_____
_____
_____
_____

Problem 9-3B

Part a.

Year	Straight-Line
2018	
2019	
2020	
2021	
TOTAL	

Part b.

Year	Double-Declining-Balance
2018	
2019	
2020	
2021	
TOTAL	

Name: _____

Problem 9-3B (concl'd.)

Part c.

Year	Units-of-Production
2018	
2019	
2020	
2021	
TOTAL	

Part d.

_____

_____

_____

_____

_____

_____

Name: _____

Problem 9-4B

Part 1 Purchased January 1

	2020	2021	2022
A. Double-declining balance method			
Machinery..	$588,000	$588,000	$588,000
Less: Accumulated depreciation................			
Year-end book value.....................................			
Depreciation expense for the year...................			
B. Straight-line method			
Machinery	$588,000	$588,000	$588,000
Less: Accumulated depreciation			
Year-end book value.....................................			
Depreciation expense for the year...................			

Part 2 Purchased April 1

	2020	2021	2022
A. Double-declining balance method			
Machinery..	$588,000	$588,000	$588,000
Less: Accumulated depreciation................			
Year-end book value.....................................			
Depreciation expense for the year...................			
B. Straight-line method			
Machinery	$588,000	$588,000	$588,000
Less: Accumulated depreciation			
Year-end book value.....................................			
Depreciation expense for the year...................			

Name: _____

Problem 9-5B

Year	Depreciation Method		
	Straight-Line	Double-Declining-Balance	Units-of-Production
2020			
2021			
2022			
2023			
2024			
2025			
Totals			

Name: _____

Problem 9-6B

| Year | Depreciation Method | | |
	Straight-Line	Double-Declining-Balance	Units-of-Production
2020			
2021			
2022			
2023			
2024			
2025			
Totals			

Calculations:

Problem 9-7B

Part 1

GENERAL JOURNAL

Page_____

Date		Account Titles and Explanation	PR	Debit	Credit

Part 2

Westfair Foods

Partial Balance Sheet

December 31, 2021

Problem 9-8B

Part 1

	Market Value	Percentage of Total	Apportioned Cost
Building			
Land			
Land improvements..............			
Truck...	_____	_____	_____
Total..	_____	_____	_____

GENERAL JOURNAL   Page_____

Date	Account Titles and Explanation	PR	Debit	Credit

Part 2: 2020 straight-line depreciation on building:

_____

_____

_____

Part 3: 2020 double-declining-balance depreciation on land improvements:

_____

_____

_____

Name: _____

Problem 9-9B

| Year | Depreciation | | |
	Straight-Line	Units-of-Production	Double-Declining-Balance
2020			
2021			
2022			
2023			
2024			
2025			
Totals			

Calculations:

Problem 9-10B

Description	Cost Information					Depreciation		
	Date of Purchase	Depreciation Method	Cost	Residual	Life	Balance of Accum. Deprec. Apr. 30, 2020	Depreciation Expense for 2021	Balance of Accum. Deprec. Apr. 30, 2021
Equipment	Oct. 3/17	Straight-line	$62,400	$16,800	20 yr.			
Machinery	Oct. 28/17	Units-of-production	540,000	180,000	100,000 units			
Tools	Nov. 3/17	Double-declining-balance	64,000	15,000	5 yr.			

Calculations:

GENERAL JOURNAL

Page_____

Date		Account Titles and Explanation	PR	Debit	Credit

Calculations:

Problem 9-12B

GENERAL JOURNAL

Page_____

Date		Account Titles and Explanation	PR	Debit	Credit

Calculations:

Problem 9-13B

Part 1: Entry to record the purchase of the new furnace:

GENERAL JOURNAL   Page____

Date	Account Titles and Explanation	PR	Debit	Credit

Calculations:

Part 2: Total depreciation expense to be recorded on the warehouse for 2020:_____

Calculations:

Windows		
Doors		
Roofing		
Siding		
Framing/Walls		
Furnace		
Misc.		
Total depreciation expense to be recorded on the warehouse for 2020 =		

Name: _____

Problem 9-14B

Part 1

GENERAL JOURNAL

Page____

Date		Account Titles and Explanation	PR	Debit	Credit

Calculations:

	Book Value	Recoverable Value	Impairment Loss
Computer equipment		$ 6,250	
Land		172,500	
Machinery		65,000	
Warehouse		243,750	

Problem 9-14B (cont'd.)

Part 2

Problem 9-14B (concl'd.)

Analysis component:
_____
_____
_____
_____
_____
_____
_____
_____
_____
_____

Problem 9-15B

Part 1   **GENERAL JOURNAL**   Page_____

Date	Account Titles and Explanation	PR	Debit	Credit

Calculations:

Problem 9-15B (cont'd.)

Part 2   **GENERAL JOURNAL**   Page____

Date	Account Titles and Explanation	PR	Debit	Credit

Calculations:

Problem 9-15B (concl'd.)

Part 3   **GENERAL JOURNAL**   Page_____

Date		Account Titles and Explanation	PR	Debit	Credit

Calculations:

Problem 9-16B

Part 1   **GENERAL JOURNAL**   Page____

Date	Account Titles and Explanation	PR	Debit	Credit

Part 2   **GENERAL JOURNAL**   Page____

Date	Account Titles and Explanation	PR	Debit	Credit

Problem 9-16B (concl'd.)

Part 3(a)   GENERAL JOURNAL   Page____

Date		Account Titles and Explanation	PR	Debit	Credit

Part 3(b)   GENERAL JOURNAL   Page____

Date		Account Titles and Explanation	PR	Debit	Credit

Part 3(c)   GENERAL JOURNAL   Page____

Date		Account Titles and Explanation	PR	Debit	Credit

Calculations:

GENERAL JOURNAL

Date	Account Titles and Explanation	PR	Debit	Credit

Calculations:

Problem 9-18B

1. Depreciation expense on first December 31 of each machine's life:

GENERAL JOURNAL

Page_____

Date		Account Titles and Explanation	PR	Debit	Credit

2. Purchase/exchange/disposal of each machine:

GENERAL JOURNAL

Page_____

Date		Account Titles and Explanation	PR	Debit	Credit

GENERAL JOURNAL

Page_____

Date	Account Titles and Explanation	PR	Debit	Credit

Calculations:

Name: _____

Problem 9-19B

1a.   GENERAL JOURNAL   Page____

Date		Account Titles and Explanation	PR	Debit	Credit

1b.   GENERAL JOURNAL   Page____

Date		Account Titles and Explanation	PR	Debit	Credit

Part 2

_____

Partial Balance Sheet

Problem 9-20B

Part 1   **GENERAL JOURNAL**   Page____

Date	Account Titles and Explanation	PR	Debit	Credit

Part 2   **GENERAL JOURNAL**   Page____

Date	Account Titles and Explanation	PR	Debit	Credit

Name: _____

*Problem 9-21B

1a. | | GENERAL JOURNAL | | | Page_____

Date	Account Titles and Explanation	PR	Debit	Credit

1b. | | GENERAL JOURNAL | | | Page_____

Date	Account Titles and Explanation	PR	Debit	Credit

Calculations:

Name: _____

*Problem 9-21B (concl'd.)

Part 2

_____

_____

Metal Frame		
Engine	2015:	
	2016:	
	2017:	
	2018:	
	2019:	
	2020:	
New Fan		
Conveyor System		
Misc. Parts	2015:	
	2016:	
	2017:	
	2018:	
	2019:	
	Total	

Fundamental Accounting Principles, 16ce, Working Papers

Quick Study AI-1

_____
_____
_____
_____
_____
_____
_____

Quick Study AI-2

GENERAL JOURNAL

Date		Account Titles and Explanation	PR	Debit	Credit

Quick Study AI-3

GENERAL JOURNAL

Date		Account Titles and Explanation	PR	Debit	Credit

Quick Study AI-4

| | | Deductions | | | | Pay | Distribution | |
Employee	Gross Pay	EI Premium	Income Taxes	CPP	Deductions Total	Net Pay	Office Salaries	Sales Salaries
Johnson, S.	1,200.00	19.92	241.15	56.07				
Waverley, N.	530.00	8.80	57.25	22.90				
Zender, B.	675.00	11.21	92.05	30.08				
Totals	2,405.00	39.93	390.45	109.05				

Quick Study AI-5

| Employee | Gross Pay | Deductions | | | | Pay | Salaries Expense |
		EI Premium	Income Taxes	CPP	Total Deductions	Net Pay	
Bentley, A.	2,010.00						
Craig, T.	2,115.00						
Totals	4,125.00						

Quick Study AI-6

| Employee | Gross Pay | Deductions | | | | Pay | Distribution | |
		EI Premium	Income Taxes	CPP	Total Deductions	Net Pay	Office Salaries	Sales Salaries
Withers, S.	2,500.00						2,500.00	
Volt, C.	1,800.00							1,800.00
Totals								

Calculations:

_____

_____

_____

_____

_____

_____

_____

_____

Quick Study AI-7

GENERAL JOURNAL   Page_____

Date	Account Titles and Explanation	PR	Debit	Credit

Quick Study AI-8

GENERAL JOURNAL

Date		Account Titles and Explanation	PR	Debit	Credit

Quick Study AI-9

GENERAL JOURNAL

Date		Account Titles and Explanation	PR	Debit	Credit

Quick Study AI-10

GENERAL JOURNAL

Date		Account Titles and Explanation	PR	Debit	Credit

Name:_____

Quick Study AI-11

GENERAL JOURNAL

Date		Account Titles and Explanation	PR	Debit	Credit

Exercise AI-1

Exercise AI-2

		Deductions					Pay
Employee	Gross Pay	EI Premium	Income Taxes	CPP	Health Insurance Deductions	Total Deductions	Net Pay
H. Craig	720.00		101.55		24.00		
J. Lim	610.00		76.60		24.00		
D. Patelli	830.00		128.20		36.00		
S. McFee	1,700.00		407.90		24.00		
Totals	3,860.00		714.25		108.00		

Calculations:

_____
_____
_____
_____
_____
_____
_____

Exercise AI-2 (concl'd.)

GENERAL JOURNAL

Date	Account Titles and Explanation	PR	Debit	Credit

Exercise AI-3

Employee	Gross Pay	EI Prem.	Income Taxes	United Way	CPP	Total Deductions	Net Pay	Admin. Salaries	Sales Salaries
Atkins, D.	1,900.00	31.54	322.25	80.00	87.39				
Nesbitt, M.	1,260.00	20.92	161.35	50.00	55.71				
Trent, F.	1,680.00	27.89	261.60	40.00	76.50				
Vallot, M.	3,000.00	49.80	680.00	300.00	141.84				
Totals	7,840.00	130.15	1,425.20	470.00	361.44				

Exercise AI-4

Employee	Gross Pay	EI Prem.	Income Taxes	Canada Savings Bonds	CPP	United Way	Total Deductions	Net Pay	Office Salaries	Sales Salaries
Crimson	1,995.00								1,995.00	
Long	2,040.00									2,040.00
Morris	2,000.00									2,000.00
Peterson	2,280.00									2,280.00
Totals	8,315.00									

Name:_____

Exercise AI-5

Employee	Gross Pay	EI Prem.	Income Taxes	Medical Ins.	CPP	United Way	Total Deductions	Net Pay	Office Salaries	Guide Salaries
				Deductions				**Payment**	**Distribution**	
Wynne	1,200.00			65.00		40.00				1,200.00
Short	950.00			65.00		100.00			950.00	
Pearl	1,150.00			65.00		0				1,150.00
Quincy	875.00			65.00		50.00				875.00
Totals	4,175.00									

Calculations:

_____
_____
_____
_____
_____
_____
_____
_____
_____
_____

Exercise AI-6

GENERAL JOURNAL

Date	Account Titles and Explanation	PR	Debit	Credit

Appendix I

Name:_____

Exercise AI-7

GENERAL JOURNAL

Date		Account Titles and Explanation	PR	Debit	Credit

Exercise AI-8

GENERAL JOURNAL

Date		Account Titles and Explanation	PR	Debit	Credit

Exercise AI-9

GENERAL JOURNAL

Date		Account Titles and Explanation	PR	Debit	Credit

Exercise AI-10

GENERAL JOURNAL

Date		Account Titles and Explanation	PR	Debit	Credit

Exercise AI-11

Employee	CPP Contribution	EI Contribution	Retirement Fund Contributions	Health Insurance

Calculations:

_____
_____
_____
_____
_____
_____
_____
_____
_____
_____

Exercise AI-12

GENERAL JOURNAL

Date	Account Titles and Explanation	PR	Debit	Credit

Exercise AI-13

GENERAL JOURNAL

Date	Account Titles and Explanation	PR	Debit	Credit

Appendix I

Name:_____

Problem AI-1A

Part 1

Employee	M	T	W	T	F	S	S	Total Hrs.	O.T. Hrs.	Reg. Pay Rate	Regular Pay	O.T. Premium Pay	Gross Pay
			Daily Time									Earnings	
Loran	8	8	8	8	8	4	0			40.00			
Sousa	7	8	6	7	8	4	0			36.00			
Smith	8	8	0	8	8	4	4			32.00			
Parton	8	8	8	8	8	0	0			40.00			
Wood	0	6	6	6	6	8	8			36.00			

Employee	EI Prem.	CPP	Income Tax	Hosp. Ins.	Union Dues	Total Deductions	Net Pay	Office Wages Expense	Service Wages Expense
			Deductions				Payment	Distribution	
Loran				40.00	16.00				
Sousa				40.00	15.00				
Smith				40.00	14.00				
Parton				40.00	16.00				
Wood				40.00	16.00				
Totals				200.00	77.00				

Part 2

GENERAL JOURNAL

Date	Account Titles and Explanation	PR	Debit	Credit

Appendix I

Name:_____

Problem AI-2A

Part 1

GENERAL JOURNAL

Date	Account Titles and Explanation	PR	Debit	Credit

Part 2

GENERAL JOURNAL

Date	Account Titles and Explanation	PR	Debit	Credit

Problem AI-3A

Part 1

GENERAL JOURNAL

Date	Account Titles and Explanation	PR	Debit	Credit

Problem AI-3A (concl.)

Part 2

GENERAL JOURNAL

Date		Account Titles and Explanation	PR	Debit	Credit

Part 3

GENERAL JOURNAL

Date		Account Titles and Explanation	PR	Debit	Credit

Problem AI-4A

GENERAL JOURNAL

Date		Account Titles and Explanation	PR	Debit	Credit

Problem AI-4A (concl.)

GENERAL JOURNAL

Date		Account Titles and Explanation	PR	Debit	Credit

Problem AI-1B

Part 1

Employee	Daily Time							Total Hrs.	O.T. Hrs.	Reg. Pay Rate	Earnings		
	M	T	W	T	F	S	S				Regular Pay	O.T. Premium Pay	Gross Pay
Amoko	8	8	8	8	8	0	0			34.00			
Carson	7	8	8	7	8	4	0			36.00			
Cheng	8	8	0	8	8	4	4			36.00			
Deszca	8	8	8	8	8	0	0			30.00			
Tan	0	6	6	6	6	8	8			30.00			

Employee	Deductions						Payment	Distribution	
	EI Prem.	CPP	Income Tax	Hosp. Ins.	Union Dues	Total Deductions	Net Pay	Office Wages Expense	Service Wages Expense
Amoko				30.00	12.00				
Carson				30.00	12.00				
Cheng				30.00	12.00				
Deszca				30.00	12.00				
Tan				30.00	12.00				
Totals				150.00	60.00				

Part 2

GENERAL JOURNAL

Date		Account Titles and Explanation	PR	Debit	Credit

Name:_____

Problem AI-2B

Part 1

GENERAL JOURNAL

Date		Account Titles and Explanation	PR	Debit	Credit

Part 2

GENERAL JOURNAL

Date		Account Titles and Explanation	PR	Debit	Credit

Problem AI-3B

Part 1

GENERAL JOURNAL

Date		Account Titles and Explanation	PR	Debit	Credit

Problem AI-3B (concl.)

Part 2

GENERAL JOURNAL

Date		Account Titles and Explanation	PR	Debit	Credit

Part 3

GENERAL JOURNAL

Date		Account Titles and Explanation	PR	Debit	Credit

Problem AI-4B

GENERAL JOURNAL

Date		Account Titles and Explanation	PR	Debit	Credit

Problem AI-4B(concl.)

GENERAL JOURNAL

Date		Account Titles and Explanation	PR	Debit	Credit

Name: _____

Quick Study AII-1

1. _____	3. _____
2. _____	4. _____

Quick Study AII-2

1. _____	5. _____
2. _____	6. _____
3. _____	7. _____
4. _____	8. _____

Quick Study AII-3

a. _____	e. _____
b. _____	f. _____
c. _____	g. _____
d. _____	

Quick Study AII-4

GENERAL JOURNAL

Page____

Date	Account Titles and Explanation	PR	Debit	Credit

Name: _____

Quick Study AII-5

1. _____	5. _____
2. _____	6. _____
3. _____	7. _____
4. _____	

Quick Study AII-6

1. _____	5. _____
2. _____	6. _____
3. _____	7. _____
4. _____	

Quick Study AII-7

Sales Journal					Page
Date	Account Debited	Invoice Number	PR	Accounts Receivable Dr. Sales Cr.	Cost of Goods Sold Dr. Merchandise Inventory Cr.

Quick Study AII-8

Cash Receipts Journal									Page
Date	Account Credited	PR	Explanation	Cash Dr.	Sales Disc. Dr.	Accts. Rec. Cr.	Sales Cr.	Other Accts. Cr.	COGS Dr. Merch. Inv. Cr.

Quick Study AII-9

Purchases Journal								Page
Date	Account Credited	Date of Invoice	Terms	PR	Accounts Payable Cr.	Merch. Inventory Dr.	Office Supplies Dr.	Other Accounts Dr.

Appendix II

Quick Study AII-10

							Page
Cash Disbursements Journal							
Date	Ch. No.	Payee	Account Debited	PR	Cash Cr.	Merch. Inventory Cr.	Other Accounts Dr.	Accounts Payable Dr.

Exercise AII-1

					Page
Sales Journal					
Date	Account Debited	Invoice Number	PR	Accounts Receivable Dr. Sales Cr.	Cost of Goods Sold Dr. Merchandise Inventory Cr.

*Exercise AII-2

				Page
Sales Journal				
Date	Account Debited	Invoice No.	PR	Accounts Receivable Dr. Sales Cr.

Exercise AII-3

									Page
Cash Receipts Journal									
Date	Account Credited	PR	Explanation	Cash Dr.	Sales Disc. Dr.	Accts. Rec. Cr.	Sales Cr.	Other Accts. Cr.	COGS Dr. Merch. Inv. Cr.

*Exercise AII-4

Cash Receipts Journal								Page
Date	Account Credited	PR	Explanation	Cash Dr.	Sales Disc. Dr.	Accts. Rec. Cr.	Sales Cr.	Other Accts. Cr.

Exercise AII-5

Purchases Journal								Page
Date	Account Credited	Date of Invoice	Terms	PR	Accounts Payable Cr.	Merch. Inventory Dr.	Office Supplies Dr.	Other Accounts Dr.

*Exercise AII-6

Purchases Journal								Page
Date	Account Credited	Date of Invoice	Terms	PR	Accts. Payable Cr.	Purchases Dr.	Office Supplies Dr.	Other Accts. Dr.

Exercise AII-7

Cash Disbursements Journal								Page
Date	Ch. No.	Payee	Account Debited	PR	Cash Cr.	Merch. Inventory Cr.	Other Accounts Dr.	Accounts Payable Dr.

*Exercise AII-8

								Page
Cash Disbursements Journal								
Date	Ch. No.	Payee	Account Debited	PR	Cash Cr.	Purch. Disc. Cr.	Other Accounts Dr.	Accts. Payable Dr.

Exercise AII-9

Part 1 – Wilson Purchasing

								Page
Purchases Journal								
Date	Account Credited	Date of Invoice	Terms	PR	Accounts Payable Cr.	Merch. Inventory Dr.	Office Supplies Dr.	Other Accounts Dr.

								Page
Cash Disbursements Journal								
Date	Ch. No.	Payee	Account Debited	PR	Cash Cr.	Merch. Inventory Cr.	Other Accounts Dr.	Accounts Payable Dr.

GENERAL JOURNAL   Page_____

Date		Account Titles and Explanation	PR	Debit	Credit

Exercise AII-9 (concl'd.)

Part 2 – Hostel Sales

	Sales Journal					Page
Date	Account Debited	Invoice Number	PR	Accounts Receivable Dr. Sales Cr.		Cost of Goods Sold Dr. Merchandise Inventory Cr.

	Cash Receipts Journal								Page
Date	Accounts Credited	PR	Explanation	Cash Dr.	Sales Disc. Dr.	Accts. Rec. Cr.	Sales Cr.	Other Accts. Cr.	COGS Dr. Merch. Inv. Cr.

GENERAL JOURNAL   Page_____

Date		Account Titles and Explanation	PR	Debit	Credit

*Exercise AII-10

Part 1 – Wilson Purchasing

	Purchases Journal							Page
Date	Account Credited	Date of Invoice	Terms	PR	Accts. Payable Cr.	Purchases Dr.	Office Supplies Dr.	Other Accts. Dr.

*Exercise AII-10 (concl'd.)

								Page
			Cash Disbursements Journal					
Date	Ch. No.	Payee	Account Debited	PR	Cash Cr.	Purch. Disc. Cr.	Other Accounts Dr.	Accts. Payable Dr.

GENERAL JOURNAL   Page____

Date		Account Titles and Explanation	PR	Debit	Credit

Part 2 – Hostel Sales

				Page
	Sales Journal			
Date	Account Debited	Invoice No.	PR	Accounts Receivable Dr. Sales Cr.

								Page
	Cash Receipts Journal							
Date	Account Credited	PR	Explanation	Cash Dr.	Sales Disc. Dr.	Accts. Rec. Cr.	Sales Cr.	Other Accts. Cr.

GENERAL JOURNAL   Page____

Date		Account Titles and Explanation	PR	Debit	Credit

Exercise AII-11

_____
_____
_____
_____
_____
_____
_____
_____
_____
_____
_____

Exercise AII-12

a. _____

b. _____

c. _____

d. _____

e. _____

Exercise AII-13

Part 1   ACCOUNTS RECEIVABLE SUBLEDGER

Sanders Farrell	Dan Holland	Brad Smithers

Part 2   GENERAL LEDGER

AccountsReceivable	Sales	Sales Returns and Allowances

Exercise AII-13 (concl'd.)

Part 3

Schedule of Accounts Receivable

*Exercise AII-14

Parts 1 and 2

GENERAL LEDGER

Cash	Accounts Payable	Sales Returns and Allowances

Accts. Receivable	Notes Payable	Purchases

Prepaid Insurance	Sales	Purchase Discounts

Store Equipment	Sales Discounts	Purchase Returns and Allowances

*Exercise AII-14 (concl'd.)

ACCOUNTS RECEIVABLE SUBLEDGER

Jack Hertz	Trudy Stone	Dave Waylon

ACCOUNTS PAYABLE SUBLEDGER

Grass Corp.	McGrew Company	Sulter Inc.

Problem AII-1A

Special Journal		Subledger	
Sales..................................	S	Accounts Receivable	AR
Purchases........................	P	Accounts Payable	AP
Cash Receipts	CR	Merchandise Inventory ...	MI
Cash Disbursements......	CD	No Effect	NE
General Journal	G		

Date	Transaction	Special Journal	Subledger
Mar. 1	*Sold merchandise on credit.*	*S*	*AR/MI*
2	Defective merchandise sold on March 1 was returned by the customer. It was scrapped.		
3	Purchased office equipment on credit; terms n/30.		
5	Received payment regarding the March 1 sale.		
10	Received a credit memo from the supplier regarding defective equipment purchased on March 3.		
14	Sold merchandise for cash.		
16	Purchased merchandise inventory on credit; terms 1/5, n/30.		
17	Paid the balance owing on the March 3 transaction.		
18	Purchased merchandise inventory for cash.		
21	Paid for the merchandise purchased on March 16.		
22	Sold old equipment for cash.		
30	Paid salaries for the month of March.		
30	Accrued utilities for the month of March.		
30	Closed the credit balance in the Income Summary to Capital.		

Problem AII-2A

Sales Journal					Page 3
Date	Account Debited	Invoice Number	PR	Accounts Receivable Dr. Sales Cr.	Cost of Goods Sold Dr. Merchandise Inventory Cr.

Cash Receipts Journal									Page 3
Date	Accounts Credited	PR	Explanation	Cash Dr.	Sales Disc. Dr.	Accts. Rec. Cr.	Sales Cr.	Other Accts. Cr.	COGS Dr. Merch. Inv. Cr.

Purchases Journal								Page 3
Date	Account Credited	Date of Invoice	Terms	PR	Accounts Payable Cr.	Merch. Inventory Dr.	Office Supplies Dr.	Other Accounts Dr.

Cash Disbursements Journal								Page 3
Date	Ch. No.	Payee	Account Debited	PR	Cash Cr.	Merch. Inventory Cr.	Other Accounts Dr.	Accounts Payable Dr.

Problem AII-2A (concl'd.)

GENERAL JOURNAL   Page_____

Date	Account Titles and Explanation	PR	Debit	Credit

Problem AII-3A   Part 1

ACCOUNTS RECEIVABLE SUBLEDGER

Paul Abrams   **ACCOUNT NO. 106-1**

DATE	EXPLANATION	PR	DEBIT	CREDIT	BALANCE

Linda Hobart   **ACCOUNT NO. 106-2**

DATE	EXPLANATION	PR	DEBIT	CREDIT	BALANCE

Kelly Schaefer   **ACCOUNT NO. 106-3**

DATE	EXPLANATION	PR	DEBIT	CREDIT	BALANCE

Problem AII-3A (cont'd.)

Part 2   **ACCOUNTS PAYABLE SUBLEDGER**

Frank's Supply   **ACCOUNT NO. 201-1**

DATE	EXPLANATION	PR	DEBIT	CREDIT	BALANCE

Baskin Company   **ACCOUNT NO. 201-2**

DATE	EXPLANATION	PR	DEBIT	CREDIT	BALANCE

Sprocket Company   **ACCOUNT NO. 201-3**

DATE	EXPLANATION	PR	DEBIT	CREDIT	BALANCE

Eau Claire Inc.   **ACCOUNT NO. 201-4**

DATE	EXPLANATION	PR	DEBIT	CREDIT	BALANCE

Problem AII-3A (cont'd.)

Part 3

				Sales Journal		Page 3
Date	Account Debited	Invoice Number	PR	Accounts Receivable Dr. Sales Cr.		Cost of Goods Sold Dr. Merchandise Inventory Cr.

			Cash Receipts Journal						Page 3
Date	Accounts Credited	PR	Explanation	Cash Dr.	Sales Disc. Dr.	Accts. Rec. Cr.	Sales Cr.	Other Accts. Cr.	COGS Dr. Merch. Inv. Cr.

Problem AII-3A (concl'd.)

					Purchases Journal			Page 3
Date	Account Credited	Date of Invoice	Terms	PR	Accounts Payable Cr.	Merch. Inventory Dr.	Office Supplies Dr.	Other Accounts Dr.

					Cash Disbursements Journal			Page 3
Date	Ch. No.	Payee	Account Debited	PR	Cash Cr.	Merch. Inventory Cr.	Other Accounts Dr.	Accounts Payable Dr.

GENERAL JOURNAL   Page____

Date	Account Titles and Explanation	PR	Debit	Credit

Problem AII-4A Parts 1, 4

GENERAL LEDGER

Cash   ACCOUNT NO. 101

DATE	EXPLANATION	PR	DEBIT	CREDIT	BALANCE
2020					
Mar. 31	Balance brought forward				167,000

Accounts Receivable   ACCOUNT NO. 106

DATE	EXPLANATION	PR	DEBIT	CREDIT	BALANCE

Merchandise Inventory   ACCOUNT NO. 119

DATE	EXPLANATION	PR	DEBIT	CREDIT	BALANCE
2020					
Mar. 31	Balance brought forward				105,000

Office Supplies   ACCOUNT NO. 124

DATE	EXPLANATION	PR	DEBIT	CREDIT	BALANCE

Store Supplies   ACCOUNT NO. 125

DATE	EXPLANATION	PR	DEBIT	CREDIT	BALANCE

Store Equipment   ACCOUNT NO. 165

DATE	EXPLANATION	PR	DEBIT	CREDIT	BALANCE

Name: _____

Problem AII-4A (cont'd)

Accounts Payable   ACCOUNT NO. 201

DATE	EXPLANATION	PR	DEBIT	CREDIT	BALANCE

Long-Term Notes Payable   ACCOUNT NO. 251

DATE	EXPLANATION	PR	DEBIT	CREDIT	BALANCE
2020					
Mar. 31	Balance brought forward				167,000

Jeff Newton, Capital   ACCOUNT NO. 301

DATE	EXPLANATION	PR	DEBIT	CREDIT	BALANCE
2020					
Mar. 31	Balance brought forward				105,000

Sales   ACCOUNT NO. 413

DATE	EXPLANATION	PR	DEBIT	CREDIT	BALANCE

Sales Discounts   ACCOUNT NO. 415

DATE	EXPLANATION	PR	DEBIT	CREDIT	BALANCE

Cost of Goods Sold   ACCOUNT NO. 502

DATE	EXPLANATION	PR	DEBIT	CREDIT	BALANCE

Sales Salaries Expense   ACCOUNT NO. 621

DATE	EXPLANATION	PR	DEBIT	CREDIT	BALANCE

Problem AII-4A (cont'd)

	Advertising Expense				ACCOUNT NO. 655
DATE	EXPLANATION	PR	DEBIT	CREDIT	BALANCE

NOTE: For Parts 2 and 3, journalizing and posting, continue journalizing the transactions in the journals provided in Problem AII-3A.

Part 5

	Trial Balance		
		Debit	**Credit**

Problem AII-4A (concl'd.)

Schedule of Accounts Receivable

Schedule of Accounts Payable

Analysis component:

_____
_____
_____
_____
_____
_____
_____
_____
_____
_____
_____
_____
_____

Problem AII-5A

Parts 1, 2, 3

Sales Journal					Page 3
Date	Account Debited	Invoice Number	PR	Accounts Receivable Dr. Sales Cr.	Cost of Goods Sold Dr. Merchandise Inventory Cr.
2020					
Oct. 6	M. Craig	913	√	3,300	1,600
12	V. Foresman	914	√	3,650	1,900
15	A. Ihrig	915	√	3,100	1,700

Purchases Journal								Page 2
Date	Account	Date of Invoice	Terms	PR	Accounts Payable Cr.	Merch. Inventory Dr.	Office Supplies Dr.	Other Accounts Dr.
2020								
Oct. 2	Shore Co.	Oct. 2	2/10,n/60	√	3,200	3,200		
5	Brown Sup.	Oct. 3	n/10,EOM	√	1,300	1,300		
15	Shore Co.	Oct. 15	2/10,n/60	√	3,990	3,990		
15	Sunshine Co	Oct. 15	2/10,n/60	√	2,650	2,650		

Fundamental Accounting Principles, 16ce, Working Papers

Problem AII-5A (cont'd.)

			Cash Receipts Journal						Page 3
Date	Account Credited	PR	Explanation	Cash Dr.	Sales Disc. Dr.	Accts. Rec. Cr.	Sales Cr.	Other Accts. Cr.	COGS Dr. Merch. Inv. Cr.
2020									
Oct. 2	B. Grigsby	√	Inv. 09/23	4,116	84	4,200			
15	Sales		Cash sales	38,830			38,830		21,400
15	M. Craig	√	Inv. 10/6	2,401	49	2,450			

			Cash Disbursements Journal					Page 4
Date	Ch. No.	Payee	Account Debited	PR	Cash Cr.	Merch. Inventory Cr.	Other Accounts Dr.	Accounts Payable Dr.
2020								
Oct. 2	619	Omni Realty	Rent Exp.	640	2,250		2,250	
6	620	Fireside Co.	Fireside Co.	√	3,724	76		3,800
12	621	Shore Co.	Shore Co.	√	3,136	64		3,200
15	622	Jamie Green	Sales Sal. Exp.	621	2,020		2,020	

Problem AII-5A (cont'd.)

GENERAL JOURNAL

Date			Account Titles and Explanation	PR	Debit	Credit
2020						
Oct.	4		Accounts Payable—Fireside Company	201/√	460	
			Merchandise Inventory	119		460
			Received a credit memo for returns.			
	9		Sales Returns and Allowances	414	850	
			Accounts Receivable—Marge Craig	106/√		850
			Issued a credit memorandum.			
	9		Merchandise Inventory	119	430	
			Cost of Goods Sold	502		430
			Merchandise returned to inventory.			

ACCOUNTS RECEIVABLE SUBLEDGER
Marge Craig

DATE		EXPLANATION	PR	DEBIT	CREDIT	BALANCE
2020						
Oct.	6		S3	3,300		3,300
	9		G2		850	2,450
	15		CR3		2,450	-0-

Vickie Foresman

DATE		EXPLANATION	PR	DEBIT	CREDIT	BALANCE
2020						
Oct.	12		S3	3,650		3,650

Problem AII-5A (cont'd.)

Parts 2 and 3

Bill Grigsby

DATE	EXPLANATION	PR	DEBIT	CREDIT	BALANCE
2020					
Sept. 23		S2	4,200		4,200
Oct. 2		CR3		4,200	-0-

Amy Ihrig

DATE	EXPLANATION	PR	DEBIT	CREDIT	BALANCE
2020					
Oct. 15		S3	3,100		3,100

ACCOUNTS PAYABLE SUBLEDGER

Fireside Company

DATE	EXPLANATION	PR	DEBIT	CREDIT	BALANCE
2020					
Sept. 28		P1		4,260	4,260
Oct. 4		G2	460		3,800
6		CD4	3,800		-0-

Brown Supply Company

DATE	EXPLANATION	PR	DEBIT	CREDIT	BALANCE
2020					
Oct. 5		P2		1,300	1,300

Sunshine Company

DATE	EXPLANATION	PR	DEBIT	CREDIT	BALANCE
2020					
Oct. 15		P2		2,650	2,650

Problem AII-5A (cont'd.)

Parts 2 and 3 (Cont'd.)

Shore Company

DATE	EXPLANATION	PR	DEBIT	CREDIT	BALANCE
2020					
Oct. 2		P2		3,200	3,200
12		CD4	3,200		-0-
15		P2		3,990	3,990

Parts 2 and 3   GENERAL LEDGER

Cash   ACCOUNT NO. 101

DATE	EXPLANATION	PR	DEBIT	CREDIT	BALANCE
2020					
Sept. 30	Balance				5,361

Accounts Receivable   ACCOUNT NO. 106

DATE	EXPLANATION	PR	DEBIT	CREDIT	BALANCE
2020					
Sept. 30	Balance				4,200
Oct. 9		G2		850	3,350

Merchandise Inventory   ACCOUNT NO. 119

DATE	EXPLANATION	PR	DEBIT	CREDIT	BALANCE
2020					
Sept. 30	Balance				66,970
Oct. 4		G2		460	66,510
9		G2	430		66,940

Name: _____

Problem AII-5A (cont'd.)

Office Supplies · ACCOUNT NO. 124

DATE	EXPLANATION	PR	DEBIT	CREDIT	BALANCE
2020					
Sept. 30	Balance				607

Store Supplies · ACCOUNT NO. 125

DATE	EXPLANATION	PR	DEBIT	CREDIT	BALANCE
2020					
Sept. 30	Balance				346

Store Equipment · ACCOUNT NO. 165

DATE	EXPLANATION	PR	DEBIT	CREDIT	BALANCE
2020					
Sept. 30	Balance				42,129

Accumulated Depreciation, Store Equipment · ACCOUNT NO. 166

DATE	EXPLANATION	PR	DEBIT	CREDIT	BALANCE
2020					
Sept. 30	Balance				9,153

Accounts Payable · ACCOUNT NO. 201

DATE	EXPLANATION	PR	DEBIT	CREDIT	BALANCE
2020					
Sept. 30	Balance				4,260
Oct. 4		G2	460		3,800

Ken Shaw, Capital · ACCOUNT NO. 301

DATE	EXPLANATION	PR	DEBIT	CREDIT	BALANCE
2020					
Sept. 30	Balance				106,200

Problem AII-5A (cont'd.)

Ken Shaw, Withdrawals — ACCOUNT NO. 302

DATE	EXPLANATION	PR	DEBIT	CREDIT	BALANCE
2020					

Sales — ACCOUNT NO. 413

DATE	EXPLANATION	PR	DEBIT	CREDIT	BALANCE
2020					

Sales Returns and Allowances — ACCOUNT NO. 414

DATE	EXPLANATION	PR	DEBIT	CREDIT	BALANCE
2020					
Oct. 9		G2	850		850

Sales Discounts — ACCOUNT NO. 415

DATE	EXPLANATION	PR	DEBIT	CREDIT	BALANCE
2020					

Cost of Goods Sold — ACCOUNT NO. 502

DATE	EXPLANATION	PR	DEBIT	CREDIT	BALANCE
2020					
Oct. 9		G2		430	(430)

Sales Salaries Expense — ACCOUNT NO. 621

DATE	EXPLANATION	PR	DEBIT	CREDIT	BALANCE
2020					
Oct. 15		CD4	2,020		2,020

Rent Expense — ACCOUNT NO. 640

DATE	EXPLANATION	PR	DEBIT	CREDIT	BALANCE
2020					
Oct. 2		CD4	2,250		2,250

Problem AII-5A (cont'd.)

Utilities Expense   **ACCOUNT NO. 690**

DATE	EXPLANATION	PR	DEBIT	CREDIT	BALANCE
2020					

Part 4

SASKAN ENTERPRISES

Trial Balance

October 31, 2020

Problem AII-5A (concl'd.)

Part 4

	SASKAN ENTERPRISES		
	Schedule of Accounts Receivable		
	October 31, 2020		

	SASKAN ENTERPRISES		
	Schedule of Accounts Payable		
	October 31, 2020		

Problem AII-6A

Sales Journal						Page
Date	Account Debited	Invoice Number	PR	Accounts Receivable Dr. Sales Cr.	PR	Cost of Goods Sold Dr. Merch. Inventory Cr.

Purchases Journal									Page
Date	Account Credited	Date of Invoice	Terms	PR	Accts. Payable Cr.	PR	Merch. Inventory Dr.	Office Supplies Dr.	Other Accounts Dr.

NOTE: An additional PR column has been added to both journals to facilitate the referencing of inventory entries into the inventory subsidiary ledger.

Problem AII-6A (concl'd.)

Inventory Subledger Record – FIFO Perpetual

Date	PR	Purchases	Sales (at cost)	Inventory Balance

Note: An additional PR column has been added to the Inventory Subledger Record to facilitate referencing of inventory entries.

*Problem AII-7A

Part 1   **ACCOUNTS RECEIVABLE SUBLEDGER**

Paul Abrams   **ACCOUNT NO. 106-1**

DATE	EXPLANATION	PR	DEBIT	CREDIT	BALANCE

*Problem AII-7A (cont'd.)

Linda Hobart   ACCOUNT NO. 106-2

DATE	EXPLANATION	PR	DEBIT	CREDIT	BALANCE

Kelly Schaefer   ACCOUNT NO. 106-3

DATE	EXPLANATION	PR	DEBIT	CREDIT	BALANCE

Part 2   ACCOUNTS PAYABLE SUBLEDGER

Frank's Supply   ACCOUNT NO. 201-1

DATE	EXPLANATION	PR	DEBIT	CREDIT	BALANCE

Baskin Company   ACCOUNT NO. 201-2

DATE	EXPLANATION	PR	DEBIT	CREDIT	BALANCE

Sprocket Company   ACCOUNT NO. 201-3

DATE	EXPLANATION	PR	DEBIT	CREDIT	BALANCE

Name: _____

*Problem AII-7A (cont'd.)

	Eau Claire Inc.				ACCOUNT NO. 201-4	
DATE	EXPLANATION	PR	DEBIT	CREDIT	BALANCE	

Part 3

		Sales Journal			Page	
Date	Account Debited		Invoice No.	PR	Accounts Receivable Dr. Sales Cr.	

		Cash Receipts Journal						Page
Date	Account Credited	PR	Explanation	Cash Dr.	Sales Disc. Dr.	Accts. Rec. Cr.	Sales Cr.	Other Accts. Cr.

Name: _____

*Problem AII-7A (concl'd.)

Purchases Journal   Page

Date	Account Credited	Date of Invoice	Terms	PR	Accts. Payable Cr.	Purchases Dr.	Office Supplies Dr.	Other Accts. Dr.

Cash Disbursements Journal   Page

Date	Ch. No.	Payee	Account Debited	PR	Cash Cr.	Purch. Disc. Cr.	Other Accounts Dr.	Accts. Payable Dr.

GENERAL JOURNAL   Page_____

Date		Account Titles and Explanation	PR	Debit	Credit

Fundamental Accounting Principles, 16ce, Working Papers

*Problem AII-8A

Parts 1 and 4   GENERAL LEDGER

Cash

ACCOUNT NO. 101

DATE	EXPLANATION	PR	DEBIT	CREDIT	BALANCE
2020					
Mar. 31					167,000

Accounts Receivable

ACCOUNT NO. 106

DATE	EXPLANATION	PR	DEBIT	CREDIT	BALANCE

Merchandise Inventory

ACCOUNT NO. 119

DATE	EXPLANATION	PR	DEBIT	CREDIT	BALANCE
2020					
Mar. 31					105,000

Office Supplies

ACCOUNT NO. 124

DATE	EXPLANATION	PR	DEBIT	CREDIT	BALANCE

Store Supplies

ACCOUNT NO. 125

DATE	EXPLANATION	PR	DEBIT	CREDIT	BALANCE

Store Equipment

ACCOUNT NO. 165

DATE	EXPLANATION	PR	DEBIT	CREDIT	BALANCE

Accounts Payable

ACCOUNT NO. 201

DATE	EXPLANATION	PR	DEBIT	CREDIT	BALANCE

Appendix II   Name: _____

*Problem AII-8A (cont'd)

Long-Term Notes Payable   ACCOUNT NO. 251

DATE	EXPLANATION	PR	DEBIT	CREDIT	BALANCE
2020					
Mar. 31					167,000

Jeff Newton, Capital   ACCOUNT NO. 301

DATE	EXPLANATION	PR	DEBIT	CREDIT	BALANCE
2020					
Mar. 31					105,000

Sales   ACCOUNT NO. 413

DATE	EXPLANATION	PR	DEBIT	CREDIT	BALANCE

Sales Discounts   ACCOUNT NO. 415

DATE	EXPLANATION	PR	DEBIT	CREDIT	BALANCE

Purchases   ACCOUNT NO. 505

DATE	EXPLANATION	PR	DEBIT	CREDIT	BALANCE

Purchases Discounts   ACCOUNT NO. 506

DATE	EXPLANATION	PR	DEBIT	CREDIT	BALANCE

Purchases Returns and Allowances   ACCOUNT NO. 507

DATE	EXPLANATION	PR	DEBIT	CREDIT	BALANCE

*Problem AII-8A (cont'd)

	Sales Salaries Expense			ACCOUNT NO. 621	
DATE	EXPLANATION	PR	DEBIT	CREDIT	BALANCE

	Advertising Expense			ACCOUNT NO. 655	
DATE	EXPLANATION	PR	DEBIT	CREDIT	BALANCE

NOTE: For Parts 2 and 3, journalizing and posting, continue journalizing the transactions in the journals provided in *Problem AII-7A.

Part 5

Trial Balance

	Debit	Credit

*Problem AII-8A (concl'd.)

Schedule of Accounts Receivable

Schedule of Accounts Payable

Fundamental Accounting Principles, 16ce, Working Papers

Problem AII-1B

Special Journal		Subledger	
Sales..................................	S	Accounts Receivable	AR
Purchases......................	P	Accounts Payable	AP
Cash Receipts	CR	Merchandise Inventory ...	MI
Cash Disbursements......	CD	No Effect	NE
General Journal	G		

Date	Transaction	Special Journal	Subledger
May 1	The owner invested an automobile into the business.		
2	Sold merchandise and received cash.		
3	Purchased merchandise inventory on credit; terms 1/5, n/30.		
4	Sold merchandise on credit.		
5	The customer of May 4 returned defective merchandise; the merchandise was scrapped.		
6	Regarding the May 3 purchase, received a credit memo from the supplier granting an allowance.		
15	Paid mid-month salaries.		
17	Purchased office supplies on credit; terms n/30.		
19	Paid for the balance owing on the May 3 purchase.		
22	Received payment on the May 4 sale.		
25	Borrowed money from bank.		
29	Purchased merchandise inventory; paid cash.		
30	Accrued interest income.		
30	Closed all revenue accounts to the Income Summary account.		

Problem AII-2B

	Sales Journal				Page S1
Date	Account Debited	Invoice Number	PR	Accounts Receivable Dr. Sales Cr.	Cost of Goods Sold Dr. Merchandise Inventory Cr.

	Cash Receipts Journal								Page CR1
Date	Accounts Credited	PR	Explanation	Cash Dr.	Sales Disc. Dr.	Accts. Rec. Cr.	Sales Cr.	Other Accts. Cr.	COGS Dr. Merch. Inv. Cr.

	Purchases Journal							Page P1
Date	Account Credited	Date of Invoice	Terms	PR	Accounts Payable Cr.	Merch. Inventory Dr.	Office Supplies Dr.	Other Accounts Dr.

	Cash Disbursements Journal							Page CD1
Date	Ch. No.	Payee	Account Debited	PR	Cash Cr.	Merch. Inventory Cr.	Other Accounts Dr.	Accounts Payable Dr.

Problem AII-2B (concl'd.)

GENERAL JOURNAL   Page____

Date	Account Titles and Explanation	PR	Debit	Credit

Problem AII-3B   Parts 2, 3, 5

Part 1   ACCOUNTS RECEIVABLE SUBLEDGER

Kelly Grody   ACCOUNT NO. 106-1

DATE	EXPLANATION	PR	DEBIT	CREDIT	BALANCE

Karen Harden   ACCOUNT NO. 106-2

DATE	EXPLANATION	PR	DEBIT	CREDIT	BALANCE

Paul Kane   ACCOUNT NO. 106-3

DATE	EXPLANATION	PR	DEBIT	CREDIT	BALANCE

Problem AII-3B (cont'd.)

Part 2

ACCOUNTS PAYABLE SUBLEDGER

Beech Company   ACCOUNT NO. 201-1

DATE	EXPLANATION	PR	DEBIT	CREDIT	BALANCE

Blackwater Inc.   ACCOUNT NO. 201-2

DATE	EXPLANATION	PR	DEBIT	CREDIT	BALANCE

Poppe's Supply   ACCOUNT NO. 201-3

DATE	EXPLANATION	PR	DEBIT	CREDIT	BALANCE

Sprague Company   ACCOUNT NO. 201-4

DATE	EXPLANATION	PR	DEBIT	CREDIT	BALANCE

Part 3

				Sales Journal	Page 3
Date	Account Debited	Invoice Number	PR	Accounts Receivable Dr. Sales Cr.	Cost of Goods Sold Dr. Merchandise Inventory Cr.

Problem AII-3B (cont'd.)

									COGS Dr.
Date	**Account Credited**	**PR**	**Explanation**	**Cash Dr.**	**Sales Disc. Dr.**	**Accts. Rec. Cr.**	**Sales Cr.**	**Other Accts. Cr.**	**Merch. Inv. Cr.**

Cash Receipts Journal — Page 3

Purchases Journal — Page 3

Date	**Account Credited**	**Date of Invoice**	**Terms**	**PR**	**Accounts Payable Cr.**	**Merch. Inventory Dr.**	**Office Supplies Dr.**	**Other Accounts Dr.**

Cash Disbursements Journal — Page 3

Date	**Ch. No.**	**Payee**	**Account Debited**	**PR**	**Cash Cr.**	**Merch. Inventory Cr.**	**Other Accounts Dr.**	**Accounts Payable Dr.**

Problem AII-3B (concl'd.)

GENERAL JOURNAL Page_____

Date		Account Titles and Explanation	PR	Debit	Credit

Problem AII-4B

Part 1, 4   **GENERAL LEDGER**

Cash   ACCOUNT NO. 101

DATE	EXPLANATION	PR	DEBIT	CREDIT	BALANCE
2020					
Jun. 30	Balance brought forward				190,000

Accounts Receivable   ACCOUNT NO. 106

DATE	EXPLANATION	PR	DEBIT	CREDIT	BALANCE

Merchandise Inventory   ACCOUNT NO. 119

DATE	EXPLANATION	PR	DEBIT	CREDIT	BALANCE
2020					
Jun. 30	Balance brought forward				334,000

Problem AII-4B (cont'd.)

Office Supplies   ACCOUNT NO. 124

DATE	EXPLANATION	PR	DEBIT	CREDIT	BALANCE

Store Supplies   ACCOUNT NO. 125

DATE	EXPLANATION	PR	DEBIT	CREDIT	BALANCE

Store Equipment   ACCOUNT NO. 165

DATE	EXPLANATION	PR	DEBIT	CREDIT	BALANCE

Accounts Payable   ACCOUNT NO. 201

DATE	EXPLANATION	PR	DEBIT	CREDIT	BALANCE

Long-Term Notes Payable   ACCOUNT NO. 251

DATE	EXPLANATION	PR	DEBIT	CREDIT	BALANCE
2020					
Jun. 30	Balance brought forward				334,000

Gene Duncan, Capital   ACCOUNT NO. 301

DATE	EXPLANATION	PR	DEBIT	CREDIT	BALANCE
2020					
Jun. 30	Balance brought forward				190,000

Problem AII-4B (cont'd.)

Sales ACCOUNT NO. 413

DATE	EXPLANATION	PR	DEBIT	CREDIT	BALANCE

Sales Discounts ACCOUNT NO. 415

DATE	EXPLANATION	PR	DEBIT	CREDIT	BALANCE

Cost of Goods Sold ACCOUNT NO. 502

DATE	EXPLANATION	PR	DEBIT	CREDIT	BALANCE

Sales Salaries Expense ACCOUNT NO. 621

DATE	EXPLANATION	PR	DEBIT	CREDIT	BALANCE

Advertising Expense ACCOUNT NO. 655

DATE	EXPLANATION	PR	DEBIT	CREDIT	BALANCE

NOTE: For Parts 2, 3, and 4, journalizing and posting, continue journalizing the transactions in the accounts provided in Problem AII-3A.

Problem AII-4B (cont'd.)

Part 5

<table>
<tr><td colspan="3" align="center">**DUNCAN INDUSTRIES**</td></tr>
<tr><td colspan="3" align="center">Trial Balance</td></tr>
<tr><td colspan="3" align="center">July 31, 2020</td></tr>
<tr><td></td><td>**Debit**</td><td>**Credit**</td></tr>
<tr><td></td><td></td><td></td></tr>
<tr><td></td><td></td><td></td></tr>
<tr><td></td><td></td><td></td></tr>
<tr><td></td><td></td><td></td></tr>
<tr><td></td><td></td><td></td></tr>
<tr><td></td><td></td><td></td></tr>
<tr><td></td><td></td><td></td></tr>
<tr><td></td><td></td><td></td></tr>
<tr><td></td><td></td><td></td></tr>
<tr><td></td><td></td><td></td></tr>
<tr><td></td><td></td><td></td></tr>
<tr><td></td><td></td><td></td></tr>
<tr><td></td><td></td><td></td></tr>
<tr><td></td><td></td><td></td></tr>
<tr><td></td><td></td><td></td></tr>
</table>

<table>
<tr><td colspan="3" align="center">**DUNCAN INDUSTRIES**</td></tr>
<tr><td colspan="3" align="center">Schedule of Accounts Receivable</td></tr>
<tr><td colspan="3" align="center">July 31, 2020</td></tr>
<tr><td></td><td></td><td></td></tr>
<tr><td></td><td></td><td></td></tr>
<tr><td></td><td></td><td></td></tr>
<tr><td></td><td></td><td></td></tr>
<tr><td></td><td></td><td></td></tr>
</table>

<table>
<tr><td colspan="3" align="center">**DUNCAN INDUSTRIES**</td></tr>
<tr><td colspan="3" align="center">Schedule of Accounts Payable</td></tr>
<tr><td colspan="3" align="center">July 31, 2020</td></tr>
<tr><td></td><td></td><td></td></tr>
<tr><td></td><td></td><td></td></tr>
<tr><td></td><td></td><td></td></tr>
<tr><td></td><td></td><td></td></tr>
<tr><td></td><td></td><td></td></tr>
<tr><td></td><td></td><td></td></tr>
</table>

Problem AII-4B (concl'd.)

Analysis component:

_____
_____
_____
_____
_____
_____
_____
_____
_____

Problem AII-5B

Part 1

				Sales Journal	Page 3
Date	Account Debited	Invoice Number	PR	Accounts Receivable Dr. Sales Cr.	Cost of Goods Sold Dr. Merchandise Inventory Cr.
2020					
Oct. 6	M. Craig	913	√	6,600	3,600
12	H. Flatt	914	√	7,300	4,000
15	A. Izon	915	√	6,200	3,400

									Cash Receipts Journal — Page 3
Date	Account Credited	PR	Explanation	Cash Dr.	Sales Disc. Dr.	Accts. Rec. Cr.	Sales Cr.	Other Accts. Cr.	COGS Dr. Merch. Inv. Cr.
2020									
Oct. 2	J. Wildman	√	Inv. 09/23	8,232	168	8,400			
15	Sales		Cash sales	77,660			77,660		42,800
15	M. Craig	√	Inv. 10/6	4,802	98	4,900			

Problem AII-5B (cont'd.)

Purchases Journal								Page 2
Date	Account Credited	Date of Invoice	Terms	PR	Accounts Payable Cr.	Merch. Inventory Dr.	Office Supplies Dr.	Other Accounts Dr.
2020								
Oct. 2	Walters Co.	10/2	2/10,n/60	√	6,400	6,400		
5	Green Supply	10/3	n/10,EOM	√	2,600	2,600		
15	Walters Co.	10/15	2/10,n/60	√	7,980	7,980		
15	Sunshine Co.	10/15	2/10,n/60	√	5,300	5,300		

Cash Disbursements Journal								Page 4
Date	Ch. No.	Payee	Account Debited	PR	Cash Cr.	Merch. Inventory Cr.	Other Accounts Dr.	Accounts Payable Dr.
2020								
Oct. 2	619	Omni Realty	Rent Exp.	640	4,500		4,500	
6	620	Fireside Co.	Fireside Co.	√	7,448	152		7,600
12	621	Walters Co.	Walters Co.	√	6,272	128		6,400
15	622	Jamie Ford	Sales Sal. Exp.	621	5,240		5,240	

Problem AII-5B (cont'd.)

GENERAL JOURNAL   Page 2

Date		Account Titles and Explanation	PR	Debit	Credit
2020					
Oct.	4	Accounts Payable—Fireside Company	201/√	920	
		Merchandise Inventory	119		920
		Received a credit memo for returns.			
	9	Sales Returns and Allowances	414	1,700	
		Accounts Receivable—Marge Craig	106/√		1,700
		Issued a credit memorandum.			

ACCOUNTS RECEIVABLE SUBLEDGER
Marge Craig

DATE		EXPLANATION	PR	DEBIT	CREDIT	BALANCE
2020						
Oct.	6		S3	6,600		6,600
	9		G2		1,700	4,900
	15		CR3		4,900	-0-

Heather Flatt

DATE		EXPLANATION	PR	DEBIT	CREDIT	BALANCE
2020						
Oct.	12		S3	7,300		7,300

Problem AII-5B (cont'd.)

Amy Izon

DATE		EXPLANATION	PR	DEBIT	CREDIT	BALANCE
2020						
Oct.	15		S3	6,200		6,200

Jan Wildman

DATE		EXPLANATION	PR	DEBIT	CREDIT	BALANCE
2020						
Sept.	23		S2	8,400		8,400
Oct.	2		CR3		8,400	-0-

ACCOUNTS PAYABLE SUBLEDGER

Fireside Company

DATE		EXPLANATION	PR	DEBIT	CREDIT	BALANCE
2020						
Sept.	28		P1		8,520	8,520
Oct.	4		G2	920		7,600
	6		CD4	7,600		-0-

Green Supply Company

DATE		EXPLANATION	PR	DEBIT	CREDIT	BALANCE
2020						
Oct.	5		P2		2,600	2,600

Sunshine Company

DATE		EXPLANATION	PR	DEBIT	CREDIT	BALANCE
2020						
Oct.	15		P2		5,300	5,300

Problem AII-5B (cont'd.)

Walters Company

DATE	EXPLANATION	PR	DEBIT	CREDIT	BALANCE
2020					
Oct. 2		P2		6,400	6,400
12		CD4	6,400		-0-
15		P2		7,980	7,980

Parts 2 and 3   **GENERAL LEDGER**

Cash   ACCOUNT NO. 101

DATE	EXPLANATION	PR	DEBIT	CREDIT	BALANCE
2020					
Sept. 30	Balance				10,722

Accounts Receivable   ACCOUNT NO. 106

DATE	EXPLANATION	PR	DEBIT	CREDIT	BALANCE
2020					
Sept. 30	Balance				8,400
Oct. 9		G2		1,700	6,700

Merchandise Inventory   ACCOUNT NO. 119

DATE	EXPLANATION	PR	DEBIT	CREDIT	BALANCE
2020					
Sept. 30	Balance				133,940
Oct. 4		G2		920	133,020

Problem AII-5B (cont'd.)

Office Supplies — ACCOUNT NO. 124

DATE	EXPLANATION	PR	DEBIT	CREDIT	BALANCE
2020					
Sept. 30	Balance				1,214

Store Supplies — ACCOUNT NO. 125

DATE	EXPLANATION	PR	DEBIT	CREDIT	BALANCE
2020					
Sept. 30	Balance				692

Store Equipment — ACCOUNT NO. 165

DATE	EXPLANATION	PR	DEBIT	CREDIT	BALANCE
2020					
Sept. 30	Balance				84,258

Accumulated Depreciation, Store Equipment — ACCOUNT NO. 166

DATE	EXPLANATION	PR	DEBIT	CREDIT	BALANCE
2020					
Sept. 30	Balance				18,306

Accounts Payable — ACCOUNT NO. 201

DATE	EXPLANATION	PR	DEBIT	CREDIT	BALANCE
2020					
Sept. 30	Balance				8,520
Oct. 4		G2	920		7,600

Problem AII-5B (cont'd.)

Marlee Levin, Capital   ACCOUNT NO. 301

DATE	EXPLANATION	PR	DEBIT	CREDIT	BALANCE
2020					
Sept. 30	Balance				212,400

Marlee Levin, Withdrawals   ACCOUNT NO. 302

DATE	EXPLANATION	PR	DEBIT	CREDIT	BALANCE
2020					

Sales   ACCOUNT NO. 413

DATE	EXPLANATION	PR	DEBIT	CREDIT	BALANCE
2020					

Sales Returns and Allowances   ACCOUNT NO. 414

DATE	EXPLANATION	PR	DEBIT	CREDIT	BALANCE
2020					
Oct. 9		G2	1,700		1,700

Sales Discounts   ACCOUNT NO. 415

DATE	EXPLANATION	PR	DEBIT	CREDIT	BALANCE
2020					

Cost of Goods Sold   ACCOUNT NO. 502

DATE	EXPLANATION	PR	DEBIT	CREDIT	BALANCE
2020					

Sales Salaries Expense   ACCOUNT NO. 621

DATE	EXPLANATION	PR	DEBIT	CREDIT	BALANCE
2020					
Oct. 15		CD4	5,240		5,240

Problem AII-5B (cont'd.)

Rent Expense   ACCOUNT NO. 640

DATE	EXPLANATION	PR	DEBIT	CREDIT	BALANCE
2020					
Oct. 2		CD4	4,500		4,500

Utilities Expense   ACCOUNT NO. 690

DATE	EXPLANATION	PR	DEBIT	CREDIT	BALANCE
2020					

Part 4

CHINA MOON PRODUCTS
Trial Balance
October 31, 2020

	Debit	Credit

Problem AII-5B (concl'd.)

CHINA MOON PRODUCTS
Schedule of Accounts Receivable
October 31, 2020

CHINA MOON PRODUCTS
Schedule of Accounts Payable
October 31, 2020

Problem AII-6B

Sales Journal						Page 1
Date	Account Debited	Invoice Number	PR	Accounts Receivable Dr. Sales Cr.	PR	Cost of Goods Sold Dr. Merch. Inventory Cr.

Purchases Journal									Page 1
Date	Account Credited	Date of Invoice	Terms	PR	Accts. Payable Cr.	PR	Merch. Inventory Dr.	Office Supplies Dr.	Other Accounts Dr.

NOTE: An additional PR column has been added to both journals to facilitate the referencing of inventory entries into the inventory subledger.

Problem AII-6B (concl'd.)

Inventory Subledger Record – Weighted Average Perpetual

Date	PR	Purchases	Sales (at cost)	Inventory Balance

Note: An additional PR column has been added to the Inventory Subledger Record to facilitate referencing of inventory entries.

*Problem AII-7B

Part 1   **ACCOUNTS RECEIVABLE SUBLEDGER**

Kelly Grody   **ACCOUNT NO. 106-1**

DATE	EXPLANATION	PR	DEBIT	CREDIT	BALANCE

Karen Harden   **ACCOUNT NO. 106-2**

DATE	EXPLANATION	PR	DEBIT	CREDIT	BALANCE

*Problem AII-7B (cont'd.)

Paul Kane   **ACCOUNT NO. 106-3**

DATE	EXPLANATION	PR	DEBIT	CREDIT	BALANCE

Part 2   **ACCOUNTS PAYABLE SUBLEDGER**

Beech Company   **ACCOUNT NO. 201-1**

DATE	EXPLANATION	PR	DEBIT	CREDIT	BALANCE

Blackwater Inc.   **ACCOUNT NO. 201-2**

DATE	EXPLANATION	PR	DEBIT	CREDIT	BALANCE

Poppe's Supply   **ACCOUNT NO. 201-3**

DATE	EXPLANATION	PR	DEBIT	CREDIT	BALANCE

Sprague Company   **ACCOUNT NO. 201-4**

DATE	EXPLANATION	PR	DEBIT	CREDIT	BALANCE

*Problem AII-7B (cont'd.)

Part 3

Sales Journal				Page 3
Date	Account Debited	Invoice No.	PR	Accounts Receivable Dr. Sales Cr.

Cash Receipts Journal								Page 3
Date	Account Credited	PR	Explanation	Cash Dr.	Sales Disc. Dr.	Accts. Rec. Cr.	Sales Cr.	Other Accts. Cr.

Purchases Journal								Page 3
Date	Account Credited	Date of Invoice	Terms	PR	Accts. Payable Cr.	Purchases Dr.	Office Supplies Dr.	Other Accts. Dr.

*Problem AII-7B (concl'd.)

							Other	Accts.
	Ch.		Account			Purch.	Accounts	Payable
Date	No.	Payee	Debited	PR	Cash Cr.	Disc. Cr.	Dr.	Dr.

Cash Disbursements Journal — Page 3

GENERAL JOURNAL   Page____

Date	Account Titles and Explanation	PR	Debit	Credit

*Problem AII-8B

Part 1   GENERAL LEDGER

Cash   ACCOUNT NO. 101

DATE	EXPLANATION	PR	DEBIT	CREDIT	BALANCE
2020					
Jun. 30	Balance brought forward				190,000

Accounts Receivable   ACCOUNT NO. 106

DATE	EXPLANATION	PR	DEBIT	CREDIT	BALANCE

*Problem AII-8B (cont'd.)

Merchandise Inventory   ACCOUNT NO. 119

DATE	EXPLANATION	PR	DEBIT	CREDIT	BALANCE
2020					
Jun. 30	Balance brought forward				334,000

Office Supplies   ACCOUNT NO. 124

DATE	EXPLANATION	PR	DEBIT	CREDIT	BALANCE

Store Supplies   ACCOUNT NO. 125

DATE	EXPLANATION	PR	DEBIT	CREDIT	BALANCE

Store Equipment   ACCOUNT NO. 165

DATE	EXPLANATION	PR	DEBIT	CREDIT	BALANCE

Accounts Payable   ACCOUNT NO. 201

DATE	EXPLANATION	PR	DEBIT	CREDIT	BALANCE

Long-Term Notes Payable   ACCOUNT NO. 251

DATE	EXPLANATION	PR	DEBIT	CREDIT	BALANCE
2020					
Jun. 30	Balance brought forward				334,000

*Problem AII-8B (cont'd.)

Gene Duncan, Capital   ACCOUNT NO. 301

DATE	EXPLANATION	PR	DEBIT	CREDIT	BALANCE
2020					
Jun. 30	Balance brought forward				190,000

Sales   ACCOUNT NO. 413

DATE	EXPLANATION	PR	DEBIT	CREDIT	BALANCE

Sales Discounts   ACCOUNT NO. 415

DATE	EXPLANATION	PR	DEBIT	CREDIT	BALANCE

Purchases   ACCOUNT NO. 505

DATE	EXPLANATION	PR	DEBIT	CREDIT	BALANCE

Purchase Discounts   ACCOUNT NO. 506

DATE	EXPLANATION	PR	DEBIT	CREDIT	BALANCE

Purchase Returns and Allowances   ACCOUNT NO. 507

DATE	EXPLANATION	PR	DEBIT	CREDIT	BALANCE

*Problem AII-8B (cont'd.)

Sales Salaries Expense   **ACCOUNT NO. 621**

DATE	EXPLANATION	PR	DEBIT	CREDIT	BALANCE

Advertising Expense   **ACCOUNT NO. 655**

DATE	EXPLANATION	PR	DEBIT	CREDIT	BALANCE

NOTE: For Parts 2 and 3, journalizing and posting, continue journalizing the transactions in the accounts provided in *Problem AII-7B.

Part 5

DUNCAN INDUSTRIES

Trial Balance

July 31, 2020

	Debit	Credit

Name: _____

*Problem AII-8B (concl'd.)

DUNCAN INDUSTRIES		
Schedule of Accounts Receivable		
July 31, 2020		

DUNCAN INDUSTRIES		
Schedule of Accounts Payable		
July 31, 2020		

Comprehensive Problem

Alpine Company - Perpetual

				Sales Journal		Page 2
Date	**Account Debited**	**Invoice Number**	**PR**	**Accounts Receivable Dr. Sales Cr.**	**Cost of Goods Sold Dr. Merchandise Inventory Cr.**	

				Purchases Journal				Page 2
Date	**Account Credited**	**Date of Invoice**	**Terms**	**PR**	**Accounts Payable Cr.**	**Merch. Inventory Dr.**	**Office Supplies Dr.**	**Other Accounts Dr.**

				Cash Receipts Journal					Page 2
Date	**Account Credited**	**PR**	**Explanation**	**Cash Dr.**	**Sales Disc. Dr.**	**Accts. Rec. Cr.**	**Sales Cr.**	**Other Accts. Cr.**	**COGS Dr. Merch. Inv. Cr.**

Name: _____

Comprehensive Problem

Alpine Company - Perpetual (Continued)

			Cash Disbursements Journal			Merch. Inventory Cr.	Other Accounts Dr.	Page 2
Date	Ch. No.	Payee	Account Debited	PR	Cash Cr.			Accounts Payable Dr.

GENERAL JOURNAL Page 3

Date	Account Titles and Explanation	PR	Debit	Credit

Comprehensive Problem

Alpine Company - Perpetual (Continued)

GENERAL JOURNAL   Page 3

Date	Account Titles and Explanation	PR	Debit	Credit

Name: _____

Comprehensive Problem

Alpine Company - Perpetual (Continued)

Date	Account Titles and Explanation	PR	Debit	Credit

Fundamental Accounting Principles, 16ce, Working Papers

Comprehensive Problem

Alpine Company - Perpetual (Continued)

Cash ACCOUNT NO. 101

DATE	EXPLANATION	PR	DEBIT	CREDIT	BALANCE
2020					
Apr. 30	Balance				50,247

Accounts Receivable ACCOUNT NO. 106

DATE	EXPLANATION	PR	DEBIT	CREDIT	BALANCE
2020					
Apr. 30	Balance				4,730

Merchandise Inventory ACCOUNT NO. 119

DATE	EXPLANATION	PR	DEBIT	CREDIT	BALANCE
2020					
Apr. 30	Balance				220,080

Office Supplies ACCOUNT NO. 124

DATE	EXPLANATION	PR	DEBIT	CREDIT	BALANCE
2020					
Apr. 30	Balance				430

Store Supplies ACCOUNT NO. 125

DATE	EXPLANATION	PR	DEBIT	CREDIT	BALANCE
2020					
Apr. 30	Balance				2,447

Comprehensive Problem

Alpine Company - Perpetual (Continued)

Prepaid Insurance   ACCOUNT NO. 128

DATE	EXPLANATION	PR	DEBIT	CREDIT	BALANCE
2020					
Apr. 30	Balance				3,318

Office Equipment   ACCOUNT NO. 163

DATE	EXPLANATION	PR	DEBIT	CREDIT	BALANCE
2020					
Apr. 30	Balance				22,470

Accumulated Depreciation, Office Equipment   ACCOUNT NO. 164

DATE	EXPLANATION	PR	DEBIT	CREDIT	BALANCE
2020					
Apr. 30	Balance				9,898

Store Equipment   ACCOUNT NO. 165

DATE	EXPLANATION	PR	DEBIT	CREDIT	BALANCE
2020					
Apr. 30	Balance				38,920

Accumulated Depreciation, Store Equipment   ACCOUNT NO. 166

DATE	EXPLANATION	PR	DEBIT	CREDIT	BALANCE
2020					
Apr. 30	Balance				17,556

Comprehensive Problem

Alpine Company - Perpetual (Continued)

Accounts Payable   ACCOUNT NO. 201

DATE	EXPLANATION	PR	DEBIT	CREDIT	BALANCE
2020					
Apr. 30	Balance				7,100

Clint Barry, Capital   ACCOUNT NO. 301

DATE	EXPLANATION	PR	DEBIT	CREDIT	BALANCE
2020					
Apr. 30	Balance				308,088

Clint Barry, Withdrawals   ACCOUNT NO. 302

DATE	EXPLANATION	PR	DEBIT	CREDIT	BALANCE
2020					

Sales   ACCOUNT NO. 413

DATE	EXPLANATION	PR	DEBIT	CREDIT	BALANCE

Sales Discounts   ACCOUNT NO. 414

DATE	EXPLANATION	PR	DEBIT	CREDIT	BALANCE

Comprehensive Problem

Alpine Company - Perpetual (Continued)

Sales Returns and Allowances — ACCOUNT NO. 415

DATE	EXPLANATION	PR	DEBIT	CREDIT	BALANCE

Cost of Goods Sold — ACCOUNT NO. 502

DATE	EXPLANATION	PR	DEBIT	CREDIT	BALANCE

Depreciation Expense, Office Equipment — ACCOUNT NO. 612

DATE	EXPLANATION	PR	DEBIT	CREDIT	BALANCE

Depreciation Expense, Store Equipment — ACCOUNT NO. 613

DATE	EXPLANATION	PR	DEBIT	CREDIT	BALANCE

Office Salaries Expense — ACCOUNT NO. 620

DATE	EXPLANATION	PR	DEBIT	CREDIT	BALANCE

Comprehensive Problem

Alpine Company - Perpetual (Continued)

Sales Salaries Expense   ACCOUNT NO. 621

DATE	EXPLANATION	PR	DEBIT	CREDIT	BALANCE

Insurance Expense   ACCOUNT NO. 637

DATE	EXPLANATION	PR	DEBIT	CREDIT	BALANCE

Rent Expense, Office Space   ACCOUNT NO. 641

DATE	EXPLANATION	PR	DEBIT	CREDIT	BALANCE

Rent Expense, Selling Space   ACCOUNT NO. 642

DATE	EXPLANATION	PR	DEBIT	CREDIT	BALANCE

Office Supplies Expense   ACCOUNT NO. 650

DATE	EXPLANATION	PR	DEBIT	CREDIT	BALANCE

Comprehensive Problem

Alpine Company - Perpetual (Continued)

Store Supplies Expense   ACCOUNT NO. 651

DATE	EXPLANATION	PR	DEBIT	CREDIT	BALANCE
2020					

Utilities Expense   ACCOUNT NO. 690

DATE	EXPLANATION	PR	DEBIT	CREDIT	BALANCE
2020					

Income Summary   ACCOUNT NO. 901

DATE	EXPLANATION	PR	DEBIT	CREDIT	BALANCE

ACCOUNTS RECEIVABLE LEDGER

NAME   Deaver Corp.

DATE	EXPLANATION	PR	DEBIT	CREDIT	BALANCE

NAME   Essex Company

DATE	EXPLANATION	PR	DEBIT	CREDIT	BALANCE

NAME   Nabors Inc.

DATE	EXPLANATION	PR	DEBIT	CREDIT	BALANCE
2020					
Apr. 28		S2	4,730		4,730

Comprehensive Problem

Alpine Company - Perpetual (Continued)

NAME   Oscar Services.

DATE	EXPLANATION	PR	DEBIT	CREDIT	BALANCE
2020					

ACCOUNTS PAYABLE LEDGER

NAME   Chandler Corp.

DATE	EXPLANATION	PR	DEBIT	CREDIT	BALANCE
2020					

NAME   Gale Inc.

DATE	EXPLANATION	PR	DEBIT	CREDIT	BALANCE
2020					

NAME   Parkay Products

DATE	EXPLANATION	PR	DEBIT	CREDIT	BALANCE
2020					
Apr. 30		P2		7,100	7,100

NAME   Thompson Supply Co.

DATE	EXPLANATION	PR	DEBIT	CREDIT	BALANCE

Comprehensive Problem

Alpine Company - Perpetual (Continued)

Alpine Company
Work Sheet
For Month Ended May 31, 2020

Account Titles	Trial Balance		Adjustments		Income Statement		Balance Sheet and Statement of Changes in Equity	
	Debit	Credit	Debit	Credit	Debit	Credit	Debit	Credit

Comprehensive Problem

Alpine Company - Perpetual (Continued)

Alpine Company			
Income Statement			
For Month Ended May 31, 2020			

Comprehensive Problem

Alpine Company - Perpetual (Continued)

Alpine Company

Statement of Changes in Equity

For Month Ended May 31, 2020

Alpine Company

Balance Sheet

May 31, 2020

Name: _____

Comprehensive Problem

Alpine Company - Perpetual (Concluded)

Alpine Company

Post-Closing Trial Balance

May 31, 2020

	Debit	Credit

Alpine Company

Schedule of Accounts Receivable

May 31, 2020

Alpine Company

Schedule of Accounts Payable

May 31, 2020

Name: _____

Comprehensive Problem

Alpine Company - Periodic

	Sales Journal			Page 2
Date	Account Debited	Invoice Number	PR	Accts. Receivable Dr. Sales Cr.

				Purchases Journal			Page 2	
Date	Account Credited	Date of Inv.	Terms	PR	Accts. Pay. Cr.	Purchases Dr.	Office Supplies Dr.	Other Accts. Dr.

			Cash Receipts Journal				Page 2	
Date	Accounts Credited	Explanation	PR	Cash Dr.	Sales Disc. Dr.	Accts. Rec. Cr.	Sales Cr.	Other Accts. Cr.

Fundamental Accounting Principles, 16ce, Working Papers

Comprehensive Problem

Alpine Company - Periodic (Continued)

			Cash Disbursements Journal					Page 2	
Date	Ch. No.	Payee	Account Debited	PR	Cash Cr.	Purch. Disc. Cr.	Other Accts. Dr.	Accts. Payable Dr.	

GENERAL JOURNAL   Page 3

Date	Account Titles and Explanation	PR	Debit	Credit

Comprehensive Problem

Alpine Company - Periodic (Continued)

GENERAL JOURNAL   Page 3

Date		Account Titles and Explanation	PR	Debit	Credit

Comprehensive Problem

Alpine Company - Periodic (Continued)

GENERAL LEDGER

Cash   ACCOUNT NO. 101

DATE	EXPLANATION	PR	DEBIT	CREDIT	BALANCE
2020					
Apr. 30	Balance				50,247

Accounts Receivable   ACCOUNT NO. 106

DATE	EXPLANATION	PR	DEBIT	CREDIT	BALANCE
2020					
Apr. 30	Balance				4,730

Merchandise Inventory   ACCOUNT NO. 119

DATE	EXPLANATION	PR	DEBIT	CREDIT	BALANCE
2020					
Apr. 30	Balance				220,080

Office Supplies   ACCOUNT NO. 124

DATE	EXPLANATION	PR	DEBIT	CREDIT	BALANCE
2020					
Apr. 30	Balance				430

Store Supplies   ACCOUNT NO. 125

DATE	EXPLANATION	PR	DEBIT	CREDIT	BALANCE
2020					
Apr. 30	Balance				2,447

Name: _____

Comprehensive Problem

Alpine Company - Periodic (Continued)

Prepaid Insurance   ACCOUNT NO. 128

DATE	EXPLANATION	PR	DEBIT	CREDIT	BALANCE
2020					
Apr. 30	Balance				3,318

Office Equipment   ACCOUNT NO. 163

DATE	EXPLANATION	PR	DEBIT	CREDIT	BALANCE
2020					
Apr. 30	Balance				22,470

Accumulated Depreciation, Office Equipment   ACCOUNT NO. 164

DATE	EXPLANATION	PR	DEBIT	CREDIT	BALANCE
2020					
Apr. 30	Balance				9,898

Store Equipment   ACCOUNT NO. 165

DATE	EXPLANATION	PR	DEBIT	CREDIT	BALANCE
2020					
Apr. 30	Balance				38,920

Accumulated Depreciation, Store Equipment   ACCOUNT NO. 166

DATE	EXPLANATION	PR	DEBIT	CREDIT	BALANCE
2020					
Apr. 30	Balance				17,556

Comprehensive Problem

Alpine Company - Periodic (Continued)

Accounts Payable   ACCOUNT NO. 201

DATE	EXPLANATION	PR	DEBIT	CREDIT	BALANCE
2020					
Apr. 30	Balance				7,100

Clint Barry, Capital   ACCOUNT NO. 301

DATE	EXPLANATION	PR	DEBIT	CREDIT	BALANCE
2020					
Apr. 30	Balance				308,088

Clint Barry, Withdrawals   ACCOUNT NO. 302

DATE	EXPLANATION	PR	DEBIT	CREDIT	BALANCE
2020					

Sales   ACCOUNT NO. 413

DATE	EXPLANATION	PR	DEBIT	CREDIT	BALANCE

Sales Discounts   ACCOUNT NO. 414

DATE	EXPLANATION	PR	DEBIT	CREDIT	BALANCE

Sales Returns and Allowances   ACCOUNT NO. 415

DATE	EXPLANATION	PR	DEBIT	CREDIT	BALANCE

Comprehensive Problem

Alpine Company - Periodic (Continued)

Purchases   ACCOUNT NO. 505

DATE	EXPLANATION	PR	DEBIT	CREDIT	BALANCE

Purchases Discounts   ACCOUNT NO. 506

DATE	EXPLANATION	PR	DEBIT	CREDIT	BALANCE

Purchases Returns and Allowances   ACCOUNT NO. 507

DATE	EXPLANATION	PR	DEBIT	CREDIT	BALANCE

Depreciation Expense, Office Equipment   ACCOUNT NO. 612

DATE	EXPLANATION	PR	DEBIT	CREDIT	BALANCE

Depreciation Expense, Store Equipment   ACCOUNT NO. 613

DATE	EXPLANATION	PR	DEBIT	CREDIT	BALANCE

Office Salaries Expense   ACCOUNT NO. 620

DATE	EXPLANATION	PR	DEBIT	CREDIT	BALANCE

Comprehensive Problem

Alpine Company - Periodic (Continued)

Sales Salaries Expense   ACCOUNT NO. 621

DATE	EXPLANATION	PR	DEBIT	CREDIT	BALANCE

Insurance Expense   ACCOUNT NO. 637

DATE	EXPLANATION	PR	DEBIT	CREDIT	BALANCE

Rent Expense, Office Space   ACCOUNT NO. 641

DATE	EXPLANATION	PR	DEBIT	CREDIT	BALANCE

Rent Expense, Selling Space   ACCOUNT NO. 642

DATE	EXPLANATION	PR	DEBIT	CREDIT	BALANCE

Office Supplies Expense   ACCOUNT NO. 650

DATE	EXPLANATION	PR	DEBIT	CREDIT	BALANCE

Comprehensive Problem

Alpine Company - Periodic (Continued)

Store Supplies Expense ACCOUNT NO. 651

DATE	EXPLANATION	PR	DEBIT	CREDIT	BALANCE
2020					

Utilities Expense ACCOUNT NO. 690

DATE	EXPLANATION	PR	DEBIT	CREDIT	BALANCE
2020					

Income Summary ACCOUNT NO. 901

DATE	EXPLANATION	PR	DEBIT	CREDIT	BALANCE

ACCOUNTS RECEIVABLE LEDGER

NAME Deaver Corp.

DATE	EXPLANATION	PR	DEBIT	CREDIT	BALANCE

NAME Essex Company

DATE	EXPLANATION	PR	DEBIT	CREDIT	BALANCE

NAME Nabors Inc.

DATE	EXPLANATION	PR	DEBIT	CREDIT	BALANCE
2020					
Apr. 28		S2	4,730		4,730

Comprehensive Problem

Alpine Company - Periodic (Continued)

NAME   Oscar Services.

DATE	EXPLANATION	PR	DEBIT	CREDIT	BALANCE
2020					

ACCOUNTS PAYABLE LEDGER

NAME   Chandler Corp.

DATE	EXPLANATION	PR	DEBIT	CREDIT	BALANCE
2020					

NAME   Gale Inc.

DATE	EXPLANATION	PR	DEBIT	CREDIT	BALANCE
2020					

NAME   Parkay Products

DATE	EXPLANATION	PR	DEBIT	CREDIT	BALANCE
2020					
Apr. 30		P2		7,100	7,100

NAME   Thompson Supply Co.

DATE	EXPLANATION	PR	DEBIT	CREDIT	BALANCE

Comprehensive Problem

Alpine Company - Periodic (Continued)

Alpine Company
Work Sheet
For Month Ended May 31, 2020

Account Titles	Trial Balance		Adjustments		Income Statement		Balance Sheet and Statement of Changes in Equity	
	Debit	Credit	Debit	Credit	Debit	Credit	Debit	Credit

Name: _____

Comprehensive Problem

Alpine Company - Periodic (Continued)

Alpine Company
Income Statement
For Month Ended May 31, 2020

Name: _____

Comprehensive Problem

Alpine Company - Periodic (Continued)

Alpine Company
Statement of Changes in Equity
For Month Ended May 31, 2020

Alpine Company
Balance Sheet
May 31, 2020

Comprehensive Problem

Alpine Company - Periodic (Concluded)

Alpine Company
Post-Closing Trial Balance
May 31, 2020

	Debit	Credit

Alpine Company
Schedule of Accounts Receivable
May 31, 2020

Alpine Company
Schedule of Accounts Payable
May 31, 2020
